INTRODUCTION TO
SABRE

VIASINC
GDS
TRAINING SYSTEM

STUDENT WORKBOOK

TRADEMARKS

VIASINC is a trademark of Vocational Instruction and Software, Incorporated. Sabre is a trademark of an affiliate
of Sabre Holdings Corporation.

Vocational Instruction and Software, Incorporated
Walnut Creek, California, U.S.A.
(+1) 925 932 0130
sales@viasinc.com
support@viasinc.com
http://www.viasinc.com
http://dlc.viasinc.com

TABLE OF CONTENTS

This workbook is designed to be used in conjunction with VIASINC's online interactive Introduction to Sabre Course. It offers additional practice and reinforcement of the material taught in each online lesson. While the majority of material is taught online, some new formats may be introduced in this book. The online lessons will be your primary learning source.

Chapter Organization

Each chapter corresponds to an online lesson, and is organized into sections as follows:

Review Questions

This section contains questions on the entries, responses, displays and concepts covered in the online lesson. It is not necessary to have access to the VIASINC GDS Training System to complete this section.

Supplementary Entries

This section covers new entries related to the entries taught in the online lesson. Not all chapters contain this section.

Exercises

The focus of this section is "hands-on" practice using the VIASINC Sabre Emulator. You will be asked to make Sabre entries taught in both the online lesson and the workbook chapter, and answer questions based on the responses. You will have a chance to build complete reservations (PNRs) and work with previously-built PNRs. You must be signed in to the VIASINC Sabre Emulator to complete this section. Please see below for information on the VIASINC Sabre Emulator.

Format Review

A list of the Sabre entries taught in the lesson.

Course Login

You should receive directions from your instructor or course facilitator on how to log into the online course. You should complete each online lesson prior to completing the exercises in this book.

VIASINC Sabre Emulator

The VIASINC Sabre Emulator is a sophisticated program which turns your PC into a simulated Sabre set. It very closely resembles live Sabre and is, by far, the best Sabre simulator available. Take advantage of this feature. If you feel confident using the VIASINC Sabre Emulator you will be confident using live Sabre.

All of the online lesson interact with the Sabre Emulator, but you may also use it in a "free-form" mode. It is accessed from anywhere within the course by using the

ABOUT THIS WORKBOOK

"Emulator" button, the "Place-->Emulator Frame" file menu option, or any of the other "Place" functions.

The Sabre Emulator will appear as a blank screen. Before you may make a Sabre entry, you must "sign in" by making the entry SI*1234 (or equivalent) and entering your password.

Going Back to the Lessons

When you're done using the emulator, you'll need to use one of the "Place" functions to go back to the lessons. These functions can be found in the toolbar, the customized button bar, or in the "Place" file menu.

Exiting the Program

When you're ready to stop training, exit the program using the "Exit" button or the "File-->Log out" menu option. When you log out, session data, such as quiz scores and last location, will be uploaded to the servers. If your session is interrupted by loss of power or Internet access your session data will not be saved. Be sure to exit at the beginning of a lesson or section.

Resuming Training

When you resume training, you'll be placed at the beginning of the lesson or section last studied. **Important!** If you exited while in the emulator, you'll be returned to the blank emulator screen. You will need to use one of the "Place" functions to return to the lessons.

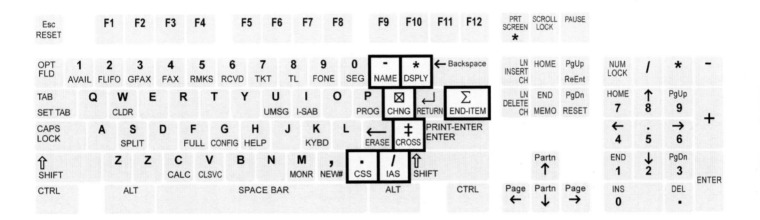

Special Character Keys

Above is an image of the Sabre keyboard. The keys outlined in black are programmed function keys used to produce characters for Sabre entries and functions. While in the VIASINC Sabre training course, your keyboard will operate like a live Sabre keyboard and these keys will produce special characters. Some of these characters are symbols unique to GDS systems, while others are found on a regular keyboard. Below is a summary of the Sabre keyboard special character keys. The symbol column shows how the character will appear in the VIASINC system; some may appear slightly different in live Sabre.

GDS Key	Symbol	Function
Display	*	Used to display a Passenger Name Record (PNR) Frequently used; appears in many GDS entries
Hyphen or "Dash"	-	Used mainly for passenger name entries and displaying profiles
Cross of Lorraine	¥	A unique GDS character used in various entries
End Item	&	Used to string multiple lines of data together as one entry. Think of this as being the word "and"
Change	¤	Used when making a change to a PNR element
Insert After	/	Used when re-arranging segments in your PNR
Segment Status Change	.	Used when airlines send schedule changes

SABRE KEYBOARD

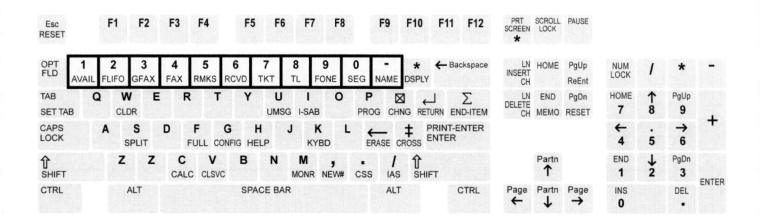

Sabre Field Identifiers

The keys at the top of the keyboard are used as the first character in many Sabre entries. They are called **ICK** or **field identifier** keys. They identify the type of Sabre entry. Below is a table of the ICK keys and their function.

Key	Function
1	Flight availability
2	Flight Information
3	Communicate or request information to/from any airline other than American Airlines
4	Communicate or request information to/from American Airlines
5	Add remarks to the Passenger Name Record (PNR)
6	Received Field of the PNR
7	Ticketing Field of the PNR
8	Used by American Airlines only
9	Phone Field of the PNR
0	Sell a product (air, car, hotel, rail, etc.)
-	Name Field of the PNR

VIASINC GDS TRAINING SYSTEM

COURSE OUTLINE

Lesson 1
Signing in and out
Introduction to the PNR
Retrieving a PNR
PNR similar name lists

Lesson 2
Encoding and decoding cities and airports
Encoding and decoding airlines
Encoding and decoding car vendors
Encoding and decoding hotels

Lesson 3
Flight availability
Flight details
Airline alliances, codeshares, low cost carriers
Air extras
Flight schedules

Lesson 4
Booking flights
Entering passenger names
Entering telephone numbers
Entering received-from data
Entering ticketing dates
Building a complete PNR
Waitlisting a flight
Entering an open segment
Entering an ARNK segment

Lesson 5
Practice building a complete PNR
End and redisplay a PNR

Lesson 6
Entering PNR remarks
Entering form-of-payment information
Entering frequent-flyer information
Entering addresses

Lesson 7
Entering Special Service Requests (SSR)
Entering Other Service Information (OSI)
TSA Secure Flight Documentation

COURSE OUTLINE

Lesson 19	Queue tasks Changing segment status Deleting a PNR segment*
Lesson 20	Number calculator Time and date calculator Temperature conversion KM/miles conversion Currency conversion FLIFO Minimum connecting times Changing areas
Lesson 21	DRS and Format Finder
Lesson 22	Timaticweb
Quiz 4	Questions on the material covered in Lessons 18 through 22
Test	Final test

* Not taught in the online lesson module.

LEARNING OUTCOMES

At the end of this lesson, you should be able to:

- Define a GDS
- Sign in to Sabre
- Sign out of Sabre
- Display a PNR
- Read a PNR
- Identify the five essential PNR fields
- Ignore a PNR

In the online lesson, you learn that Sabre is a computer reservations system called a Global Distribution System (GDS) that is used by airlines, hotels, car vendors, railways, travel agents and other travel companies to create and manage booked reservations. Because Sabre is shared by hundreds of thousands of people, users must sign in to the system to both gain access and to identify themselves so that their work can be properly tagged. In the lesson, you learn about the very important Passenger Name Record (PNR). A PNR is the record of a passenger's reservation. It is stored in Sabre's database, with a copy sent to the airline's (or hotel, car or rail company's) computer system. A PNR can be for a single passenger or a group of passengers traveling together, and it must always contain at least five pieces of information (name, itinerary, phone contact, ticketing date and received-from), though most will have much more data. Each type of information is stored in a "field" of the PNR.

When you "display" a PNR, you are making an entry to retrieve it from the Sabre database. Once it is retrieved it can be worked on (by changing a flight, adding a special meal request, etc.) or ignored. It's important to ignore a PNR that you have displayed but not altered on because it clears the PNR from the work area. It's a bit like removing an important paper from your desk when you are finished with it, so that it does not get mixed up with any new papers you may pull from a file.

Workbook Notes

In this workbook lesson, you will answer questions on the concepts and entries you learn in the online lesson. If you have trouble answering these questions, please return to the online lesson for review. You may wish to make notes in this workbook as you work online. You may access the online lesson as much as you wish, using the double-arrow toolbar buttons to go backwards for review, and forwards to return to your previous location. Note that your account may have a time restriction, which can be viewed using the "Tools-->Show Time Remaining" or "Help-->About" file menu option in the lesson.

After completing the review questions, you'll be asked to sign in to the Sabre Emulator to complete exercises, working in the same manner as you would on the live Sabre GDS system. If you make a mistake with a format, you'll receive only the Sabre error message, which can be very cryptic. Working in the emulator can be frustrating, but please keep with it. Practice is the best way to master the system, and the more work you do in the emulator, the more comfortable you will be on live Sabre.

Review Questions

Sign In and Out

1. You have just started your morning at the travel agency when a corporate client calls to check a reservation. What sign-in entry must be made before retrieving the client's PNR? Use your student ID code.

   _____

2. When you have finished work for the day, what entry signs you out of Sabre?

   _____

PNR Display

3. Many Sabre entries begin with an "identification code key" (ICK) which tells the computer what kind of action you want it to perform. What is the ICK that tells Sabre that you want to display a PNR?

   _____

4. What is the entry to display a PNR for a passenger with last name Donaldson?

   _____

5. What entry redisplays the entire PNR on your computer screen?

   _____

6. Ms. Susan Fitch just called to double check her flight times. You retrieved her PNR and reviewed all details with her. You did not make any changes to the PNR. What entry should you make to clear the work area?

   _____

7. When a Sabre display iis too long to fit on the computer screen a "¥" character appears in the lower-right corner. What entry scrolls down the display?

   _____

PNR Fields

```
1.1MILLER/MARIA MS  2.1TISSLER/CARRIE MS
 1 AA   3Q 08DEC 3 JFKLAX HK2 1200N  232P /DCAA*QHJEQV /E
 2 AA  32Q 13DEC 1 LAXJFK HK2  100P  912P /DCAA*QHJEQV /E
TKT/TIME LIMIT
  1.TAW11NOV/
PHONES
  1.JFK212-849-0181-A
  2.JFK212-785-7654-H MS MILLER
  3.JFK212-545-6484-B MS MILLER
REMARKS
  1.-CHECK
RECEIVED FROM - MS MILLER
A0A0.A0A0*ASD 1010/07NOV QHJEQV
```

The following five questions are based on the above Sabre PNR.

8.   How many passengers are in this PNR? What are their names?

    _____

9.   Fill in the following information for the first (outbound) flight of this itinerary.

    Airline _____

    Flight number _____

    Booking code _____

    Departure date _____

    Departure day of the week _____

    Departure city _____

    Arrival city _____

    Number of seats _____

    Departure time _____

    Arrival time _____

10.   On what date are the passengers returning to New York (JFK)?

    _____

11. There are three phone numbers in this PNR. The first one is for the travel agency. The other two are for . . .

_____

12. The ticket for this PNR will be issued on what date?

_____

13. The first letters of each essential PNR field form the word "PRINT". What are these fields?

"P" _____

"R" _____

"I" _____

"N" _____

"T" _____

Record Locator

```
1.1FORBES/RICHARD MR
 1 UA 538F 26MAR 7 ORDIAD HK1  0800 1039 /DCUA*BBD5WE /E
 2 UA 911F 05APR 3 IADORD HK1  1655 1751 /DCUA*BBD5WE /E
TKT/TIME LIMIT
  1.TAW17NOV/
PHONES
  1.ORD312-324-7341-A
  2.ORD312-555-3854-B
REMARKS
  1.ARRANGE LIMO PICK-UP AT IAD
RECEIVED FROM - SEC
A0A0.A0A0*AQN 0754/09NOV NKOYLE
```

The following question is based on the above Sabre PNR.

14. What is the Sabre record locator for this PNR?

_____

Auxiliary Itinerary Segments

```
1.1FARLEY/SUSAN MS
 1 UA2236Y 20MAY 6 SFOLAX HK1  0855 1024 /DCUA*898221 /E
 2 HHL BW HK1 LAX IN20MAY 6-OUT27MAY    7NT   1160 AIRPORT PLAZA
   1A2QRAC-1/74.00USD/C24H/AGT987654321/GDPST/SI-CF-S7DS6L3D
 3 UA2018Y 27MAY 6 LAXSFO HK1  1005 1131 /DCUA*898221 /E
TKT/TIME LIMIT
  1.TAW13MAY/
PHONES
  1.SFO415 555-1919-A
  2.SFO415 555-2927-H
RECEIVED FROM - P
A0A0.A0A0*AAB 1548/10APR GKILFF
```

The following question is based on the above Sabre PNR.

15. This PNR has three segments in the itinerary. The first and third segments are for flights on United Airlines (UA). What is the second segment for?

_____

Similar Name List

```
*-JONES
   A0A0-JONES
 1    JONES/MARK M  29NOV-30NOV   2    JONES/RUSSEL  26MAR-05APR
 3    JONES/RANDAL  17NOV-27NOV
```

The following question is based on the above Sabre similar name list.

16. What entry displays the PNR for Mr. Russell Jones departing on March 26?

_____

Supplementary Entries

PNR Display

In the online lesson, you learned that when you display a PNR by last name, there may be more than one PNR that matches and Sabre will display a similar name list. You may include the passenger's first name or departure date in your entry to make a more specific request, and possibibly avoid a similar name list.

`* - S M I T H / B R U C E`
This entry is used to display a PNR by both last name and first name. It is the standard entry you learned in the lesson, with a slash and the passenger's first name added to the end. This entry is less likely to generate a similar name list than an entry specifying only a last name.

`* - 1 2 J U N - S M I T H`
This entry will display a PNR by departure date and last name. It consists of the display ICK (*), followed by a hyphen, the departure date, another hyphen and the passenger's last name. This entry is especially useful when displaying a PNR for a businesss traveler for whom you have made multiple bookings.

Exercises

The questions in this section require the use of the VIASINC Sabre Emulator. To access the emulator, log into your training account and use one of the "Place" functions to move to the emulator, which will appear as a mostly blank screen onto which you'll type in commands. When you're finished using the emulator, you'll need to move back to the lessons using one of the "Place" functions.

I.   Sign in to Sabre. What entry did you make?

_____

II. Display the PNR for passenger Andrews.

Who called the travel agency to request this reservation?

_____

Whose phone number is the second listed in the phone field?

_____

Ignore the PNR to clear the work area.

III.   Mrs. Nash has called your travel agency to find out when she can pick up the ticket documents for her family's trip to Europe. Display the PNR and read the ticketing field to find out when the tickets are scheduled to be issued. If you get a similar name list, display the correct PNR from the list.

On what date should Mrs. Nash come into the travel agency to get the ticket documents?

_____

Ignore the PNR to clear the work area.

IV.   Mr. Collins has called your travel agency with a question. He would like to know if a hotel has been booked for his stay in Brussels (BRU). Retrieve his PNR.

Has a hotel been booked?

_____

Ignore the PNR to clear the work area.

V.   Ms. Andrea Weber has phoned the travel agency to ask that you no longer call her at work. You need to make sure her reservation shows her home (H) telephone number, and not her business (B) telephone number.

Display the PNR for Ms. Weber. If you get a similar name list, display the correct PNR from the list.

What can you tell Ms. Weber about the telephone numbers in the PNR?

_____

_____

Ignore the PNR to clear the work area.

VI.   Display the PNR for passenger Smith, departing a week from Monday (if today is Monday, a week from today). Use the entry to retrieve a PNR by departure date.

What is the two-letter code of the airline flying this itinerary?

_____

What is the record locator of this PNR?

_____

Ignore the PNR to clear the work area.

VII. British Airways has called concerning a reservation for your clients traveling to London and Paris. They have a copy of the reservation in their database, and have given you the Sabre record locator, UJKMUO, as the reference to the booking. Display the PNR by record locator.

Who are the passengers in this PNR?

_____

Suppose you have answered British Airways' questions without making any changes. Ignore the PNR to clear the work area.

VIII. Retrieve the PNR for passenger Mr. Randal Jones using both first and last names in your entry.

What entry did you make? _____

What does the remark say in this PNR?

_____

What is the response if you try to sign out of Sabre without ignoring this PNR?

_____

Ignore the PNR to clear the work area.

IX. Sign out of Sabre. What entry did you make?

_____

Format Review

Sign In / Out	SI*1234	Sign in to the Sabre system
	SO*	Sign out of the Sabre system
PNR Display	*-ROBERTS	Retrieve the PNR for passenger Roberts
	*1	Display the PNR numbered 1 on a similar name list
	*MMJDSB	Retrieve the PNR with record locator D348FU
	*-SMITH/BRUCE	Retrieve the PNR for passenger Bruce Smith
	*-12JUN-SMITH	Retrieve the PNR for passenger Smith departing June 12
	*A	Redisplay the current PNR
	*FF	Display the frequent flyer field
Scrolling	MD	Move down a Sabre display to see more
	MU	Move back up the display
PNR Ignore	I	Ignore the current PNR and clear the work area without making changes

LESSON **TWO**

LEARNING OUTCOMES

At the end of this lesson, you should be able to:

•**Understand the importance of codes**
•**Use the encode and decode entries**
•**Begin to memorize some airport and airline codes**

The travel industry relies heavily on a standardized set of codes, used to quickly and unambiguously identify everything from an airport to a vehicle type. In the online lesson, you learn how to "encode" airport, city, car and hotel company names to find their two- or three-character codes. You learn the reverse function of "decoding" to determine what a code represents.

It is important to have a strong knowledge of these codes. As you work through the lessons, you'll be exposed to many different airline, city and airport codes. Test your memory by trying to remember these codes. Use the Sabre Emulator to practice encoding and decoding cities which interest you.

It is worth discussing the difference between a city code and an airport code. Every city worldwide is identified with a three-letter code. If a city has only one airport, the airport will usually use the same code. If a city has two or more airports, each airport will have a unique code, often based on the airport's name. For example, the city code for New York City is NYC. The three airports servicing the city are John F. Kennedy International Airport (JFK), LaGuardia International Airport (LGA) and Newark International Airport (EWR). You'll find that many people use the term "city code" to refer to either an airport code or a city code.

Review Questions

Encode and Decode

1. What entry displays the city code for Boston?

   _____

2. What entry displays the airport code for O'Hare Airport?

   _____

3. What entry can you make to find out which city has the code "HOT"?

   _____

4. What entry tells you what airline has the code "AZ"?

   _____

5. What entry encodes Singapore Airlines?

   _____

6. Your client would like to book a rental car from Budget. What entry can you make to determine Budget's two-letter code?

_____

7. You just displayed a PNR with a car segment showing car vendor code "ZL". What entry will display the name of the car company assigned to this code?

_____

8. Your colleague has booked a hotel for one of your clients. The hotel segment shows the code "WI". What entry will display the hotel chain name corresponding to this code?

_____

9. What entry encodes Marriott Hotels?

_____

Exercises

Remember that the Exercise questions require the use of the VIASINC Sabre Emulator. Don't forget to sign in to the emulator before beginning the exercises, and to sign out after finishing the last problem.

I. What is the city code for Paris, France?

_____

What is the name of the airport in Paris with code CDG?

_____

What is the airport code for Orly Airport, also located in Paris, France?

_____

II. Encode the following:

The city of Newcastle, England _____

The town of Pickle Lake _____

Mirabel Airport _____

Royal Nepal Airlines _____

Alamo Rent A Car _____

Sheraton Hotels _____

III.   Decode the following airline and airport codes:

FI _____

VS _____

RDV _____

HKG _____

IV.   Ms. McGinty has forgotten the airline on which she is flying. Retrieve her PNR and determine the airline's name. What is the name of this airline?

_____

Where is Ms. McGinty going? _____

Where does her trip originate? _____

Ignore the PNR.

V.   In which city would you find . . .

Narita Airport _____

Haneda Airport _____

VI.   For additional practice, find the codes and names discussed in each review question.

Format Review

Encode and Decode

W/-CCPERTH	Display the three-letter city code for Perth
W/-APGATWICK	Display the three-letter airport code for Gatwick Airport
W/*LHR	Display the name of the city/airport with code LHR
W/-ALDELTA	Display the two-letter code for Delta Airlines
W/*BA	Display the name of the airline with code BA
W/-CRHERTZ	Display the code for the car company Hertz
W/CR*ZE	Display the name of the car company with code ZE
W/-HLHYATT	Display the chain code for Hyatt hotels
W/HL*FS	Display the name of the hotel chain with code FS
W/EQ-BOEING	Display the code for Boeing aircraft
W/EQ*M80	Display the name of the aircraft equipment with code M80
HCCARIZONA	Display the code for the state named Arizona
HCCMI	Display the name of the state with code MI
HCCC/AUSTRIA	Display the code for the country named Austria
HCCC/IT	Display the name of the country with code IT

LESSON **THREE**

LEARNING OUTCOMES

At the end of this lesson, you should be able to:

- Display flight availability
- Interpret flight availability displays
- Understand the concept of return availability
- Display a flight schedule
- Display availability for airlines belonging to an alliance
- Understand what a codeshare is
- Understand what a low-cost carrier is
- Retrieve an Air Extras display
- Display flight details

Flight availability (also called City Pair Availability or CPA) is the most frequently used GDS entry. When working in the industry, you'll need to process transactions quickly to obtain the high volume that is key to making money as a travel agent. Mastering flight availability entries and displays will help you immensely in this goal. The Sabre flight database is huge. The key to working efficiently with this data is to first narrow the search for an appropriate flight; second, accurately interpret the data in the display; and third, effectively communicate the flight options to your client.

The VIASINC Sabre Emulator contains every scheduled flight in the world, uploaded directly from OAG (Official Airline Guide), the same source that provides flight data to each GDS system. Take advantage of this huge database by practicing different flight availability entries in the emulator. Display flight availability from your hometown to different cities around the world. You can use the encode/decode entries in the emulator to determine the code for any airline, city or airport in the world.

Remember that you may go back into the online lesson to review the flight availability display explanations. Make notes in this workbook if you need a memory aid.

Review Questions

Flight Availability

1. What entry displays availability from Vancouver (YVR) to Miami (MIA) on June 15 at 9:00 a.m.?

_____

```
15JUN  THU    YVR/PST    MIA/EST¥3
1AA   184  F7 Y7 W7 B7 H7 Q7 YVRMIA   1300 2145    757 L  0 DCA /E
           M7 K7 V7 G7
2AA   344  F7 Y7 W7 B7 H7 Q7 YVRMIA   0715 1822    757 B/S 1 DCA /E
           M7 K7 V7 G7
3DL  1784  F7 Y7 B7 M7 K7 L7 YVRATL   1230 1955    757 D  0 DCA /E
           H7 Q7
4DL  1728  F7 Y7 B7 M7 K7 L7    MIA 4 2125 2312    767    0 X67 DCA /E
           H7 Q7
5DL  1784  F7 Y7 B7 M7 K7 L7 YVRATL   1230 1955    757 D  0 DCA /E
           H7 Q7
6DL  1490  F7 Y7 B7 M7 K7 L7    MIA 5 2310 0040¥1  M88   0 DCA /E
           H7 Q7
```

The following five questions are based on the above Sabre availability display.

2. How many nonstop flights operate between Vancouver (YVR) and Miami (MIA) on June 15?

    _____

3. What flight makes one stop en route?

    _____

4. What is the time difference between Vancouver and Miami?

    _____

5. At what airport do the flights on lines 3 and 4 connect?

    _____

6. What are the departure and arrival times for the connection on lines 3 and 4?

    _____

```
24SEP  FRI    IAD/EST    LHR/¥5
1BD/UA 4462 C4 D4 Y4 B4 IADLHR 0929 2155    763 L0 0 DC /E
            M4 H4 Q4 V4 W4
2UA     922 F7 P9 C9 D9*IADLHR 0929 2155    763 LL/LS 0 DCA /E
            Z9 Y9 B9 E9 M9 U9 H9 Q9 V9 W9 A9 S9 T9 K9
3BA     224 F9 J9 W9 Y9*IADLHR 0750 1950    777 M 0 35 DCA /E
            A9 C9 D9 R9 E9 T9 B9 H9 I9 K9 M9 V9 L9 S9
4BD/UA 4468 C4 D4 Y4 B4 IADLHR 1804 0620¥1 777 DB 0 DC /E
            M4 H4 Q4 V4 W4
5UA     918 F7 P9 C9 D9*IADLHR 1804 0620¥1 777 DB/DS 0 DCA /E
            Z9 Y9 B9 E9 M9 U9 H9 Q9 V9 W9 A9 S9 T9 K9
6BD/UA 4460 C4 D4 Y4 B4 IADLHR 1826 0655¥1 763 DB 0 DC /E
            M4 H4 Q4 V4 W4
* - FOR ADDITIONAL CLASSES ENTER 1*C
```

The following question is based on the above Sabre availability display.

7. Answer the following questions about the flights in this display.

    For the codeshare flights on lines 1, 4 and 6, "BD" is the airline selling the flight. Which airline actually operates the flight?

    _____

Which flights arrive in London (LHR) the day after they depart Washington, DC (IAD), and how can you tell?

_____

_____

Which flight operates only on Wednesdays (3) and Fridays (5)?

_____

```
18FEB   FRI    JFK/EST     SFO/PST-3
1UA    11 P4 C4 Y4 B4 M4 H4 JFKSFO 6 0700 1016  762 BS 0 DCA /E
          Q4 V4
2AA    59 P7 C7 Y7 W7 B7 V7 JFKSFO 5 0800 1057  763 B 0 DCA /E
          Q7 M7 K7 H7 G7
3UA   809 F4 C4 Y4 B4 H4 Q4 JFKSFO 5 0800 1119  762 BS 0 DCA /E
          M4 V4
4UA   988 P4 C4 Y4 B4 M4 H4 JFKSFO 4 0900 1220  762 BS 0 DCA /E
          Q4 V4
5AA    15 P7 C7 Y7 W7 B7 V7 JFKSFO 4 1100 1354  767 L 0 X67 DCA /E
          Q7 M7 K7 H7 G7
6UA     5 P4 C4 Y4 B4 M4 H4 JFKSFO 8 1205 1515  762 L 0 DCA /E
          Q4 V4
```

The following three questions are based on the above Sabre availability display.

8.   Your client would like a flight departing slightly later than the last flight listed in the above display. What entry displays later flights?

_____

9.   After making several entries to display more availability, you now want to go back to the original screen of availability. What entry should you make?

_____

10. You have just redisplayed Mr. Phillips' itinerary to review the flights you are booking. If he changes his mind and decides to take an earlier flight, what entry redisplays the last availability screen that is no longer visible in the work area?

_____

11. What entry displays availability for United (UA) flights only, from San Francisco (SFO) to New York (JFK) on April 30 at 7:00 a.m.?

_____

Return Availability

12. What entry displays return availability for February 22 at 6:00 p.m.?

_____

13. What entry displays return availability at 8:00 p.m. for the same day as the outbound?

_____

14. What entry displays return availability for the same time as the outbound availability, on August 31?

_____

Flight Details

15. Your client wants to know how long it takes to fly to New York and if dinner is served on the evening flights. You have an availability display on your screen which lists several possible flights. What entry can you make to answer your client's questions for the flight on line 2?

_____

Shortcut Entries

16. What shortcut entry changes an availability display to ...

Show departures at 3:00 p.m.? _____

Show departures on November 18? _____

Show departures at 3:00 p.m. on November 18? _____

Show departures two days later? _____

Show flights operated by Delta (DL) only? _____

Flight Schedule Displays

17. What entry displays a flight schedule for October 31 from San Francisco (SFO) to New Orleans (MSY) at 5:00 p.m.?

_____

Airline Alliances

18. What is an airline alliance?

_____

19. Name the three major airline alliances.

_____

_____

20. What entry displays availability from Atlanta (ATL) to Paris, de Gaulle (CDG) on October 23 at 6:00 p.m., showing airlines that belong to the SkyTeam ("S") alliance?

_____

Codeshares

21. In a codeshare, the ... ... is the airline that actually operates the flight, using their aircraft, equipment, crew, etc., and the ... ... is the airline whose code or brand is on the flight.

_____

Air Extras

22. Name three examples of chargeable services.

_____

23. What characters appear after a flight's booking codes if air extras are available?

_____

Supplementary Entries

**Flight
Availability**

The flight availability entries you learn in the online lesson are sufficient to book a reservation, but as you become more proficient in Sabre, you will find some advanced entries useful. The entries shown in this section are used to reduce the number of flights listed in the display, so that only the most suitable flights for your client are shown.

115MAYYYZLAX4P/D
This entry retrieves availability for direct flights only. Its purpose is to suppress all connections and list only nonstop and direct flights making one or more stops. The format is the standard availability entry with a slash (/) and the letter "D" for "direct" added to the end.

115MAYSFOMIA4P-Q
This entry is used to retrieve flights with seats available in the specified booking code. All other booking codes will be suppressed. The entry is the standard availability entry with a hyphen (-) and the booking code added to the end. This entry is useful when you are searching for a discounted booking code that is highly booked and difficult to find, something that often occurs at peak travel times such as Christmas or Thanksgiving.

103FEBMIASEA11ADFW
This entry retrieves availability specifying a connection point. Its purpose is to limit the availability display so that only connections via the specified airport are listed. The format is the standard availability entry with the three-letter airport code of the connect point added to the end. This entry is useful when a lower fare is available through the specified city, or a passenger wishes to avoid a certain airport. The departure time is mandatory in this entry.

Exercises

Don't forget to sign in to the emulator before beginning the exercises, and to sign out after finishing the last problem.

I.   Your client, who lives in San Francisco, is planning a business trip to London and Hong Kong. Use encode and decode entries to find any city and airline codes with which you are not familiar.

LESSON **THREE**

Your client is a member of British Airways' frequent flyer program and would like to fly on BA from San Francisco to London, Heathrow. Display availability for British Airways flights only, for travel the third Saturday from today. What entry did you make?

_____

How many direct flights does British Airways offer on this day? _____

Your client would like to take a direct flight from Heathrow to Hong Kong six days after her departure from San Francisco, on any airline that departs at around 2:00 p.m.

What entry did you make? _____

What airline has a flight that arrives close to 8:30 a.m.? _____

On what day does this flight arrive in Hong Kong? _____

Your client will fly back home to San Francisco six days after her departure from London. She would like the flight that connects in Los Angeles leaving Hong Kong around 4:30 p.m.

What entry did you make to display these flights? _____

What are the airline and flight numbers of the first connecting flights?

_____

II. Display flight availability for travel from San Francisco to John F. Kennedy Airport in New York for this Saturday, departing around 3:00 p.m. Display flights which have seats available in "Y".

What is the airline and flight number of the flight departing closest to 3:30 p.m.?

_____

Now your client would like to know what flights depart in the evening. Redisplay availability to list flights departing around 8:00 p.m.

What flight leaves at 10:30 p.m.? _____

Make the entry to return to the original availability screen, the one showing flights departing around 3:00 p.m.

What entry did you make? _____

Your client has decided to depart the next day. Redisplay the availability showing flights the next day.

What is the second flight listed? _____

Your client will return to San Francisco 5 days later, at 9:00 a.m. Make the return availability entry.

What entry did you make? _____

If you are located in the U.S., what flight or flights have the best on-time performance?

_____

III. Display availability of direct flights from Atlanta to Paris de Gaulle for the second Monday from today around 9:00 a.m.

What is the total travel time for Delta flight 22? _____

What meals are served on this flight in first class? _____

What time does US 754 depart Atlanta? (Hint: Use the 1* entry to display more flights.)

_____

Where does this flight stop? _____

What is the total flight time for this flight? _____

Is this flight time the total journey time? (Hint: Does it include the time spent at the connection airport?)

_____

What meals are served on the second leg of this flight in first class?

_____

Format Review

Flight Availability	115JUNJFKLAX8A	Display flight availability on June 15 from JFK to LAX at 8:00 a.m.
	115JUNORDFC0	Display flight availability with no time specified — flights departing around 1:00 p.m. will be displayed
	115JUNJFKLAX8A¥UA	Display flights operated by UA only
	115JUNORDFC08ALHR	Display flights connecting in LHR only, departure time is mandatory
	115JUNJFKLAX8A/D	Display direct flights only
	115JUNJFKLAX8A-Q	Display flights with seats available in Q booking code only
Follow-up	1*	Display the next screen of availability
	VA*2	Display flight service details for the flight listed on line 2 of availability
Redisplay	1*R	Redisplay the current screen of availability
	1*0A	Redisplay the original screen of availability
	1*9A	Redisplay, showing flights departing at 9:00 a.m.
	112JUN	Redisplay, showing flights departing on June 12
	112JUN*9A	Redisplay, showing flights departing on June 12 at 9:00 a.m.
	1¥UA	Redisplay, showing flights operated by UA only
	1¥5	Redisplay, showing flights departing five days later
	1-6	Redisplay, showing flights departing six days earlier

Return Availability	1R24JUL2P	Display return availability on July 24 at 2:00 p.m.
	1R	Display return availability for the same day
	1R3P	Display return availability for the same day at 3:00 p.m.
	1R18JAN	Display return availability for the same time on January 18
Flight Schedule Display	S13MARSFOLAX7A	Display a schedule of flights between SFO and LAX on March 13 at 7:00 a.m.
	S13MARSFOLAX7A¥AA	As above, for AA flights only
Airline Alliances	115MARFRADUS6P¥/*O	Display availability from FRA to DUS on March 15 at 6:00 p.m, showing airlines that belong to the oneworld ("O") alliance
Air Extras	1*A	Retrieve an Air Extras display for the current availability

LESSON **FOUR**

LEARNING OUTCOMES

At the end of this lesson, you should be able to:

- Sell a flight
- Create a name field
- Create a telephone field
- Create a received-from field
- Create a ticketing field
- Build a complete PNR
- "End" and save a PNR
- Waitlist a flight
- Enter an open segment
- Enter an ARNK segment

In this lesson, you learn how to build Passenger Name Records (PNRs) with the five "essential" (mandatory) fields of information. Every PNR must have at least one item in each of these fields, but in practice, most PNRs will have information in other fields as well (which you will learn about later in the course).

The first character of a Sabre entry is called the "ICK" or field identifier (see page vi). Notice that the entries to create the mandatory PNR fields all begin with a number.

Most PNR fields can contain more than one item of information. For example, you can have four telephone numbers, two passenger name items, etc. A few, however, are single item fields, such as the ticketing field and the received-from field. The number of items in a field is important when changing and deleting information, which you will learn about in a later lesson.

Review Questions

Flight Sell

```
15APR   SAT    LHR/Z¥Ø     NBO/¥3
1KQ   1Ø3  J4  Y4                LHRNBO   1815  Ø64Ø¥1  313  1 6 /E
2LH  4Ø29  C4  V4  B4  L4  K4  G4  LHRFRA  Ø7ØØ  Ø93Ø     32S  B Ø DCA /E
           M4  Q4  Z4  W4  H4  T4
3LH   58Ø  F2  C4  V4  B4  L4  K4     NBO   1Ø5Ø  195Ø     31Ø  LS Ø 56 DCA /E
           G4  M4  Q4  Z4  W4  H4  T4
4KL   11Ø  C7  S4  M7  B7  H7  Q7  LHRAMS  Ø65Ø  Ø9ØØ     737  B/S Ø DCA /E
           L4  V7
5KL   565  C7  S4  M7  B7  H7  Q7     NBO   1Ø45  2Ø15     M11  DS/DM Ø 6 DCA/E
           V7
```

The following three questions are based on the above Sabre availability display.

1. What entry books three seats in business class ("J") on the direct flight from London, Heathrow (LHR) to Nairobi (NBO)?

    _____

2. What two entries could be used to sell two seats in "B" on the Lufthansa (LH) connection from London to Nairobi?

    _____

    _____

3. For the KLM (KL) flights, how do you book one seat in "L" on the first leg and one seat in "V" on the second leg?

_____

4. How do you display just the itinerary of a PNR?

_____

```
1 KQ 1Ø3J 15APR 6 LHRNBO SS2  1815 Ø64Ø  16APR 7
```

The following two questions are based on the above Sabre flight sell response.

5. What does the status code "SS" indicate?

_____

6. Why are there two dates in the response?

_____

Name Field

7. Assume that you have just started to build a PNR for your client, Mrs. Bernadette Svensen, and her 8-year-old daughter, Rhonda. After the flights are booked, the next step is to add the name field. How would you add the passenger names?

_____

8. How do you know that a name field entry has been accepted by Sabre?

_____

9. What entries add the names Ms. Ros Needham and Mr. Joseph Mimnagh to the name field of a PNR?

_____

10. What entry displays just the name field of a PNR?

_____

`1.2MARGOLIN/STEVE MR/JANET MRS`

The following two questions are based on the above Sabre name field.

11. What does the "1" in the above name field indicate?

_____

12. What does the "2" in the above name field indicate?

_____

Phone Field

13. What entry adds the business number (212) 275-2282, extension 333, to a PNR?

_____

```
1.1BAUER/THOMAS MR   2.1DAVIDSON/JAMES MR
 1 US 929Y 20MAY 6 SFOHNL SS2  1255 1520 /DCUS /E
 2 US 928Y 27MAY 6 HNLSFO SS2  1640 0029  28MAY 7 /DCUS /E
```

The following two questions are based on the above partial Sabre PNR.

14. What entry adds the agency telephone number 415 469-1244?

_____

15. What entry adds Mr. Bauer's home telephone number, 415 676-9800, and includes his name?

_____

16. How do you display just the phone field of a PNR in the work area?

_____

Ticketing Field

17. What entry adds the ticketing date of May 15 to a PNR?

_____

18. In the above entry, TAW stands for . . .

_____

19. Your client, Mr. Wilkins, has just rushed into your agency to book flights for a trip to Chicago departing this evening. What entry would you make to indicate immediate ticketing?

_____

20. How do you display just the ticketing field of a PNR?

_____

Received-from Field

21. What is the purpose of a received-from field?

_____

_____

22. Ms. Sarah Lowe has called to make a reservation for Mr. Nick Price. What is the received-from entry for this PNR?

_____

23. How do you display just the received-from field of a PNR?

_____

End Transaction

24. What is the final step in building a PNR and what is the entry used to do this?

_____

E OK 1616 S7DS6M

The following question is based on the above Sabre end transaction response.

25. In the above response, what is "S7DS6M"?

_____

Supplementary Entries

Long Sell   ØBA282F2ØDECYYZLHRNN2

The entry shown above is used to book a flight directly, without an availability display in the work area. This entry is useful when you know the airline and flight number of the flight you wish to book.

The format of the entry is the sell ICK "Ø" followed by the airline, flight number, booking code, date of travel, departure airport, arrival airport and "NN" followed by the number of seats required. "NN" is the action code for "Need Need" and is used to request space on the flight.

Exercises

Don't forget to sign in to the emulator before beginning the exercises, and to sign out after finishing the last problem.

I.   Mr. and Mrs. Nikiforus would like to travel from Birmingham, England to da Vinci Airport in Rome four weeks from this Saturday for a two-week stay. Book flights for them in "Q" on KLM Royal Dutch Airlines.   They prefer afternoon departures.

What flights did you book for travel to Rome?   _____

What are the return flights?   _____

How many segments did you book?   _____

What is the status code for these flights?   _____

Ignore the flights you booked.

II.   Mr. and Mrs. Willowby and their two children (aged 1 and 5) would like to fly from Toronto, Ontario (Pearson Airport) to Victoria, British Columbia (International Airport). They prefer to travel in business ("J") class. Book flights for the Willowbys for travel to Victoria the fourth Friday from today, returning ten days later, with connections in Vancouver in both directions. When "J" booking code is not available, book "Y". They would like their flights to depart around 8:00 a.m.

What airline and flight numbers did you book for the Willowbys....

on the trip to Victoria? _____

on the return trip home? _____

Which segments had to be booked in "Y"? _____

How many seats did you book? _____

Ignore the flights you booked.

III. Make the two entries to add the names Mr. George and Mrs. Emily Buyers and their children, Anna (age 10) and Abby (age 1), to a PNR.

What entries did you use?

_____

_____

Make the entry "*N". Explain the characters that appear before Abby's name in the name field.

_____

Add the agency number 555-9190. Use your own area code.

Again using your own area code, add the Buyers' home telephone number, 222-8989, and Mrs. Buyers' business number, 223-0890, extension 222.

What entries did you make?

_____

_____

Make the entry to display the phone field. What entry did you make?

_____

Ignore this partial PNR.

IV.   Make the entry to book one "C" seat on Air France flight 1981 from London, Heathrow to Paris, de Gaulle on July 15. Enter an ARNK segment because the passenger will be renting a car and driving to Nice. For the return, enter an open segment on Air France in "C" from Nice to London, Heathrow. Use July 25 for the date.

What entries did you make?

_____

_____

Display the itinerary and then write down what the second and third segments look like.

_____

_____

Ignore the itinerary you booked.

V.   Make the entry to display availability for the seventh Saturday from today, for travel from New Orleans to Miami, at 8:00 a.m.

What booking code is sold out on AA flight 526? _____

Just for practice, try booking one seat in the sold-out booking code. What is the response?

_____

Waitlist one seat in the sold-out booking code. What entry did you make?

_____

Redisplay the itinerary. What is the status code of this waitlisted segment?

_____

Ignore the flight you waitlisted.

Format Review

Flight Sell

Ø1Y2	Book 1 "Y" seat from the flight on line 2 of an availability display
Ø1F1*	Book 1 "F" seat from the connection on lines 1 and 2 of an availability display
Ø1F1P2	Book 1 "F" seat from the first leg of the connection on line 1 and 1 "P" seat on the second leg of the connection on line 2 of an availability display
*I	Display the itinerary of the current PNR
ØBA282F2ØDECYYZLHRNN2	Sell 2 "F" seats on BA flight 282 from YYZ to LHR on December 20

Waitlisting

Ø2F4LL	Waitlist 2 "F" seats on the flight on line 4 of an availability display
Ø2Y1Y2LL	Waitlist 2 "Y" seats on the connection on lines 1 and 2 of an availability display

Open Segments

ØACOPENY2JUNYULYQBDS1	Enter an open segment for 1 "Y" seat on AC for travel on 2 June from YUL to YQB
Ø**OPENY2JUNSYDLHRDS1	Enter an open segment for 1 "Y" seat on any airline on 2 June from SYD to LHR (international segments only)

ARNK

ØA	Enter an ARNK segment

Name Field

-SOMERSET/LAURA MS	Enter the name of Ms. Laura Somerset
-2LOPEZ/MARCUS MR/KIMBERLY MRS	Enter two passengers with the same last name
-I/MORRIE/ISLA MISS	Enter an infant name

	*N	Display the name field of the current PNR
Phone Field	9904 540-0180-A	Enter an agency (A) phone number
	9403 680-0180-H	Enter a home (H) phone number
	9602 790-0810-B	Enter a business (B) phone number
	9602 555-2000X401-B	Enter a business (B) phone number with an extension
	9204 540-0180-B LEE	Enter a business (B) phone number belonging to passenger LEE
	*P9	Display the phone field of the current PNR
Ticketing Field	7TAW23JUN/	Enter a ticketing date of 23 June
	7T-A	Enter a ticketing arrangement for immediate ticketing
	*P7	Display the ticketing field of the current PNR
Received-from Field	6SECRETARY	Enter received-from data
	*P6	Display the received-from field of the current PNR
End Transaction	E	End transaction and save the current PNR in the database

LEARNING OUTCOMES

At the end of this lesson, you should be able to:

•Build a complete PNR
•End and redisplay a PNR

At this point, you should be familiar with the five mandatory fields of a PNR (name field, itinerary, phone field, ticketing arrangement field and received-from field) and the entries used to create each field. This lesson is devoted to using the entries together to build PNRs.

Your success as a travel agent depends on being able to quickly and efficiently process client requests. Every PNR you build and ticket will generate income for you and/or your travel company. The quicker you build each PNR, the more revenue you will generate. Using the commands in a GDS like Sabre is still the fastest way to process reservations. With practice, these commands become familiar and easy. Remember, take advantage of the VIASINC Sabre Emulator to sharpen your skills.

In the VIASINC Sabre Emulator, the PNRs you build and end will not be saved unless your instructor has turned on the "PNR Save Enable" feature. If you have a printer hooked up to your computer, you may print out your PNRs. Be sure to designate a printer using the "Edit-->Student Settings" file menu option.

In this workbook lesson, you'll learn the "ER" command which is used to end and redisplay a PNR at the same time. Agents use this command to check their work, and you can use it in the emulator to see what your PNR looks like after it has been ended.

Supplementary Entries

End Transaction

ER

In the online lesson, you practice the "E" entry after you create PNRs with the five required elements. When you end a PNR, it disappears from the screen to be stored in the database.

Sometimes you may wish to review a PNR immediately after you end it. The entry "ER" will simultaneously end and redisplay a PNR. This single entry is more efficient than the two separate entries to end transaction and then retrieve the PNR from the Sabre database.

The entry is the standard end transaction entry, E, followed by the letter "R" for "redisplay" or "retrieve".

Exercises

Don't forget to sign in to the emulator before beginning the exercises, and to sign out after finishing the last problem.

I.   Ms. Mary Hansen of Vancouver has called to make arrangements for her upcoming business trip to London, England. She wishes to depart for London, Heathrow the third Wednesday from today and return eight days later. Both segments should be Air Canada direct flights in booking code "B". Ms. Hansen's home telephone number is 604 631-0967. Your travel agency number is 604 930-1173. The airline has advised that the tickets must be issued one week prior to departure. Enter this date in the ticketing arrangement field. Build and end this PNR, answering the following questions as you go along.

What entries did you make to display availability and book the flights?

_____

What entry did you make to enter the passenger's name?

_____

What entries did you make to enter the phone numbers?

_____

What entry did you make to enter the ticketing arrangement field?

_____

What name did you enter for the received-from?

_____

What is the last entry you made?

_____

II. Mr. Ross Hanig has come into your Denver travel agency. He has just found out that he will be able to join three of his friends for a trip to New York two

weeks from Saturday. His friends already have reservations aboard the following flights:

Frontier Airlines flight 516, two weeks from Saturday, Denver to New York, LaGuardia
Frontier Airlines flight 511, 10 days later, New York, LaGuardia to Denver

Book Mr. Hanig "Y" seats on the same flights, either selling from availability or by making long sell entries. Your agency telephone number is 303 565-8822. Mr. Hanig's home telephone number is 303 807-3345. He will pick up the ticket documents this afternoon, so you will be issuing the tickets immediately. Build and then end and retrieve this PNR. Answer the following questions as you go along.

After you have booked the flights, display the itinerary. What is the status code of the segments?

_____

What entry did you make to add the ticketing arrangement field?

_____

What is the record locator of this PNR? _____

What is the new status code of the segments after the PNR is redisplayed?

_____

Ignore the PNR.

III. Alice and Paul Rogers would like to travel from Honolulu to Minneapolis to visit relatives. They prefer to fly on Delta. Mrs. Rogers tells you that they wish to leave a week from next Tuesday, in the late evening. They would like to return the following Sunday, and since they will be tired, they prefer a direct flight. To qualify for the lowest fare, the flights should be booked in booking code "B" and the tickets must be issued one week prior to departure.

Their home telephone number is 808 243-1212 and Alice's business number is 808 244-7070. The agency number is 808 222-1092.

Build the PNR, answering the following questions as you go along.

Does Delta Airlines have nonstop service from Honolulu to Minneapolis on the day your clients wish to depart?

_____

Where does Delta flight 1151 from Minneapolis to Honolulu stop?

_____

What entry did you make to enter the business telephone number?

_____

What is the PNR's record locator?

_____

Format Review

End Transaction	E R	End and redisplay a PNR simultaneously

LEARNING OUTCOMES

At the end of this lesson, you should be able to add the following items to a PNR:

• **Remark**
• **Form-of-payment remark**
• **Frequent-flyer number**
• **E-mail address**
• **Mailing address**
• **Agency address**

The five mandatory fields provide only the minimum amount of information required by Sabre to complete a PNR. Most PNRs will contain many other fields of information. In this lesson, you'll begin to learn about some of these fields.

Remember that, in general, the more information you store in a PNR, the better service you offer your customer. If every PNR you build contains your client's frequent-flyer number, your client will be saved the hassle of asking the airline to add it to his booking when he checks in. Likewise, storing your client's credit card information in the remarks field will make issuing a ticket quick and easy. Recording a client's e-mail address means you can easily send a copy of the trip itinerary to her. The benefits are numerous, and the more you practice the entries to add this information to a PNR, the easier they become.

Review Questions

PNR Remarks

1. List four different uses of a PNR remark.

    _____

    _____

    _____

2. What is the ICK used in remarks entries?

    _____

3. What entry adds the remark "BOOK RENTAL CAR" to a Sabre PNR?

    _____

4. Your clients are flying to Europe. What entry adds the remark "VALID PASSPORTS REQUIRED" to the PNR so that it will print on the clients' itinerary?

    _____

5. What entry displays the remarks field of a PNR?

    _____

Form-of-Payment Remark

6. What is the purpose of a form-of-payment remark?

   _____

   _____

7. Beside each of the following forms of payment, write the entry you would make to add the form-of-payment remark.

   Check _____

   Cash _____

8. What are the two-letter codes for the following credit cards?

   MasterCard _____

   Visa _____

   American Express _____

   Diner's Club _____

9. What entry adds Visa card number 4510 6788 8888 9999, expiring in December of next year, to a PNR?

   _____

Frequent-Flyer Field

10. What is the purpose of the frequent-flyer field and why is it important?

    _____

    _____

11. Could the entry FFAC124893451 be used to enter the Air Canada (AC) frequent-flyer number for the second passenger in a PNR? If no, why not?

    _____

    _____

```
1.1VALKENBURG/CATHERINE MS   2.2QUINTEN/BRIAN MR/WENDY MRS
```

The following two questions are based on the above Sabre name field.

12. What two different entries could you use to add Mr. Quinten's Qantas (QF) frequent-flyer number 8789878 to a PNR you are booking?

_____

_____

13. What two different entries would add Ms. Valkenburg's United (UA) Mileage Plus frequent-flyer number 4912347 to the same PNR?

_____

_____

```
FREQUENT TRAVELER
  1.AA FB23873            HK AA    1.1 ACKERMAN/STEVE MR
```

The following two questions are based on the above Sabre frequent-flyer field.

14. To whom does this frequent-flyer number belong?

_____

15. What is the airline associated with this AAdvantage frequent-flyer number, and what is the number?

_____

```
1.1WILLENS/HEATHER MS
 1 BA 287F 19NOV 5 LHRSFO HK1   1330 1625  /DCBA*2QI109 /E
 2 DL 331F 21NOV 7 SFOLAX HK1   1130 1240  /DCDL*JLA000 /E
 3 BA 268F 23NOV 2 LAXLHR HK1   2110 1525   24NOV 3 /DCBA*2QI109 /E
TKT/TIME LIMIT
  1.TAW14NOV/
PHONES
  1.LHR0171 909 1893-A
  2.LHR0171 958 1827-H
FREQUENT TRAVELER DATA EXISTS *FF TO DISPLAY ALL
RECEIVED FROM - P
A0A0.A0A0*AHJ 1452/20OCT DMJMXT
```

The following question is based on the above Sabre PNR.

16. What is the entry to display frequent-flyer data for this PNR?

_____

**Mailing
Address**

17. Why would you need to enter a passenger's address into a PNR?

_____

18. Why would you need to enter an agency address into a PNR?

_____

19. The home address for your clients, Mr. and Mrs. Delaney, is 125 Lone Pine Street, Chicago, IL. 60601. What entry adds this address to a PNR?

_____

_____

20. Your agency address is Faraway Travel, 555 Madison St., Chicago, IL. 60601. What entry adds this address to a PNR?

_____

_____

21. What entry displays just the agency address field of the current PNR?

_____

E-Mail Address

22. What character must precede and follow the e-mail address in the "PE" entry?

_____

23. What entry will add the e-mail address "smith55@mac.com" to a PNR?

_____

```
*N
 1.3YEE/YAN MR/KATHY MRS/KEVEN MSTR
```

The following question is based on the above Sabre name field.

24. Kathy Yee has requested an e-mailed copy of the itinerary. What entry will add e-mail "kathy.yee@yeeyoung.com" to the PNR, referencing her name number?

_____

Exercises

Don't forget to sign in to the emulator before beginning the exercises, and to sign out after finishing the last problem.

I. Add the following information to the PNR for Mr. and Mrs. Beal. Record each entry you use.

The Beals live at 18 Maple Dr., San Francisco, CA. 94114.

_____

_____

The agency address is Global Travel, One Embarcadero, Suite 320, San Francisco CA. 94112.

_____

_____

Mr. Beal's United Airlines Mileage Plus number is 9809999.

_____

Mr. and Mrs. Beal would like a copy of the itinerary e-mailed to each of them individually. Mr. Beal's e-mail is "cwb@horton.com". Mrs. Beal's e-mail is "lgb16@hotmail.com". Be sure to include passenger association in each entry.

_____

_____

Add a reminder to yourself to book the Ritz Hotel in London for the clients.

_____

Display the following fields of the Beal PNR. Record each entry that you use.

Display the agency address field. _____

Display the frequent-flyer number. _____

Display the e-mail field. _____

Display the remarks field. _____

Enter a received-from (Mr. Beal) and end the PNR to save the changes.

II. Retrieve the PNR for Mr. Andrade and add the following information. Record each entry you use.

Mr. Andrade lives at 60 Lakepark Gate, Beverly Hills, CA. 90210.

_____

_____

Mr. Andrade's Delta Premier frequent-flyer number is 12345555.

_____

The passenger will be paying by Visa card number 4520 1234 1234 1234, expiring in January next year.

_____

Include a remark to print on the itinerary wishing the passenger a good trip.

_____

Enter a received-from (passenger) and end the PNR to save the changes.

III. Mrs. Bagwell has called your agency. She can't remember if she gave you her home address or her office address to mail the ticket documents. She lives on 5th Street and works on Park Avenue. Retrieve the PNR to check the address in the remarks field.

Which address did Mrs. Bagwell give you?

_____

Mrs. Bagwell remembers giving you her American Airlines frequent-flyer number, but does not recall if she gave you her husband's or her friends' numbers. Are all the frequent-flyer numbers recorded in the PNR?

_____

What is Mr. Bagwell's number?

_____

Since you haven't made any changes, ignore the PNR.

Format Review

Remarks	`5BOOK HOTEL IN MIA`	Enter a remark into a PNR
	`5¥VISA REQUIRED`	Enter an itinerary remark into a PNR
	`*P5`	Display the remarks field of the current PNR
Form-of-Payment Remark	`5-*VI4182111222333¥06/17`	Enter a credit card form of payment (VISA card 4182 111 222 333, expiring in June 2017)
	`5-CHECK`	Enter a check form of payment
	`5-CASH`	Enter a cash form of payment
Frequent-Flyer Field	`FFDL8934055952`	Enter a Delta (DL) frequent-flyer number (single-passenger PNR)
	`FFAA83B21F9-1.1`	Enter an American (AA) frequent-flyer number for passenger 1.1
	`FFAA83B21F9-VACAKIS/ANA MS`	Enter an American (AA) frequent-flyer number for passenger Ms. Ana Vacakis
Mailing Address	`5/MR JOHN WANG&5/1420 BANCROFT ST&5/VANCOUVER BC V5B 1G3`	Enter a mailing address
	`W-GOLDEN GATE TRAVEL¥291 LOMBARD ST¥SAN FRANCISCO CA 94112`	Enter an agency address
	`*PAD`	Display the agency address field
E-mail Address	`PE¥PBROWN@YAHOO.COM¥`	Enter an e-mail address

PE¥PBROWN@YAHOO.COM¥TO/PAM BROWN

        Enter an e-mail address with "TO" field

PE¥PBROWN@YAHOO.COM¥CC/TOM BROWN

        Enter an e-mail address with "CC" field (can also use "BC")

PE¥PBROWN@YAHOO.COM¥FR/JOE LING, CTC

        Enter an e-mail address with "FROM" field

PE¥DAH@CDR.COM¥WORK EMAIL

        Enter an e-mail address with free text

PE¥TRAVELGAL@MAC.COM¥-1.3

        Enter an e-mail address with passenger association (can specify name number or the exact characters from the name field; i.e., -SMITH/JANE MS)

*PE

        Display the e-mail field

LESSON **SEVEN**

LEARNING OUTCOMES

At the end of this lesson, you should be able to:

•Understand the difference between **GFAX** and **AFAX**
•Understand the difference between **OSI** and **SSR**
•Create an **OSI**
•Create an **SSR**
•Enter TSA secure flight documentation

This lesson covers OSI and SSR messages, which are simply notes or requests for the airline(s) in the itinerary. Collectively, OSI and SSR messages are called GFAX messages and are stored in the GFAX field of a PNR. Sabre has a quirk, though, and unlike all other GDSs, it requires messages sent to American Airlines to be formatted a bit differently. (Recall that Sabre started as the computer system for American Airlines.) Messages sent to American Airlines are called "AFAX".

It is important to understand the difference between an OSI message and an SSR message:

OSIs ("Other Service Information") contain information regarding the passenger (language issues, VIP status, nervous flyer, etc.)

SSRs ("Special Service Request") are requests for services for a passenger (special meals, wheelchair assistance, bulky baggage, unaccompanied minor assistance, etc.)

GFAX (and AFAX) are similar to remarks (which you learned about in the last lesson), but with a very important difference: remarks are intended for travel agent personnel only and are not transmitted to the airlines.

Review Questions

GFAX and AFAX

1. What is the ICK used for all GFAX OSI and SSR entries?

    _____

2. What is the ICK used for all AFAX OSI and SSR entries?

    _____

3. Explain the main difference between OSI/SSR messages and remarks.

    _____

    _____

4.   Explain the difference between OSI and SSR messages.

_____

_____

5.   Mrs. Jones has a pet chihuahua that she would like to carry on board the aircraft, rather than check as baggage. Would this be recorded as an OSI or SSR message?

_____

6.   What entry redisplays the AFAX field of a PNR?

_____

7.   What entry redisplays the GFAX field of a PNR?

_____

Other Service Information (OSI)

```
1.1SMITH/THEODORE MR
 1 AA1358Y 20AUG 7 SFOBOS SS1   1057 2209 /DCAA /E
 2 UA  37Y 27AUG 7 BOSSFO SS1   1700 2029 /DCUA /E
A0A0.A0A0*AAB 1655/10JUL
```

The following two questions are based on the above partial Sabre PNR.

8.   Mr. Smith is traveling to Boston (BOS) to attend the funeral of a very close family member. What entry advises American Airlines (AA) that the passenger is traveling for compassionate reasons?

_____

9.   What entry or entries advises all airlines that Mr. Smith is a nervous flyer?

_____

_____

```
1.1JONES/BENJAMIN MR  2.1DE WINTER/JACQUES MR
 1 AA   3Y 20MAR 1 JFKLAX SS2  1200 1432 /DCAA /E
 2 UA 888Y 27MAR 1 LAXSFO SS2  1305 1425 /DCUA /E
 3 DL1984Y 31MAR 5 SFOJFK SS2  0750 1615 /DCDL /E
A0A0.A0A0*AAB 1656/10FEB
```

The following two questions are based on the above partial Sabre PNR.

10. What entry advises American Airlines that Mr. Jones is a first-time flyer?

_____

11. What single entry advises both Delta and United that Mr. de Winter speaks French only?

_____

Special Service Request (SSR)

12. When you make an SSR entry, the computer reads information from two fields of the PNR, placing this information in the SSR field. What are these two fields?

_____

```
1.2FARNSWORTH/JONATHAN MR/JENNIFER MRS
 1 AA   39F 31DEC 5 SFOHNL SS2  0900 1107 /DCAA /E
 2 AA   28F 15JAN 6 HNLSFO SS2  1315 2057 /DCAA /E
A0A0.A0A0*AAB 1657/10NOV
```

The following two questions are based on the above partial Sabre PNR.

13. What entry reserves low-fat meals (LFML) for Mr. and Mrs. Farnsworth on both flights?

_____

14. What entry arranges wheelchair assistance (WCHR) for Jennifer on both flights?

_____

```
1.2PENNYCOOK/PHILIP MR/KAREN MRS
 1 DL4872Y 10FEB 4 YYZJFK SS2   1425 1655 /DCDL /E
 2 DL4878Y 14FEB 1 JFKYYZ SS2   1735 2025 /DCDL /E
A0A0.A0A0*AAB 1658/10JAN
```

The following question is based on the above partial Sabre PNR.

15. Mr. Pennycook would like a vegetarian vegan meal (VGML) on the return flight only. What single entry makes this request?

_____

```
1.1LAYTON/DIANA MISS
 1 UA1718Y 15NOV 1 YVRSEA SS1   1245 1331 /DCUA /E
 2 UA1938Y 30NOV 2 SEAYVR SS1   1340 1432 /DCUA /E
A0A0.A0A0*AAB 1659/10OCT
```

The following question is based on the above partial Sabre PNR.

16. Miss Diana Layton is an unaccompanied minor, aged 10. Make the entry to alert the airline.

_____

```
1.2ING/PERRY MR/DIANE MRS   2.2CHEN/TERRENCE MR/SUZANNE MRS
 1 UA1236Y 14FEB 1 DENDFW SS4   1240 1531 SPM /DCUA /E
 2 AA2035Y 19FEB 6 DFWIAH SS4   0640 0737 /DCAA /E
 3 AA2072Y 19FEB 6 IAHDFW SS4   1932 2042 /DCAA /E
 4 UA1501Y 28FEB 1 DFWDEN SS4   1530 1625 SPM /DCUA /E
TKT/TIME LIMIT
  1.TAW07FEB/
PHONES
  1.DEN303 871-1291-A
  2.DEN303 746-1128-H ING
  3.DEN303 980-1123-B MR CHEN
AA FACTS
  1.OSI FIRST TIME FLYER-2.1
GENERAL FACTS
  1.SSR VLML UA NN1 DENDFW1236Y14FEB
  2.SSR VLML UA NN1 DFWDEN1501Y28FEB
  3.OSI UA FIRST TIME FLYER-2.1
RECEIVED FROM - MR ING
A0A0.A0A0*AAB 1700/10JAN
```

The following two questions are based on the above Sabre PNR with AFAX and GFAX field.

17. Vegetarian meals (VLML) have been requested for segments . . .

_____

18. Whom do the OSI messages concern?

_____

TSA Secure Flight Documentation

19. Many PNRs require a "DOCS" SSR message to record extra passenger information. When is this required?

_____

_____

20. In the DOCS format, which passenger information is mandatory and which passenger information is optional?

    Full name (including middle name) _____

    Gender _____

    Date of birth _____

    Country of citizenship _____

    Passport number, expiration date and country of issue _____

21. When is the DOCO SSR entry used?

_____

_____

Exercises

Don't forget to sign in to the emulator before beginning the exercises, and to sign out after finishing the last problem.

I.   Retrieve the PNR for passenger Andrews and take the following actions. Record each entry that you use and redisplay the PNR frequently to double check your work.

Request a Kosher meal (KSML) for Mr. Andrews on both flights.

_____

Inform the airline that Mr. Ryan is president of VIASINC Travel.

_____

Inform the airline that Mr. Andrews is blind (BLND).

_____

Display the GFAX messages. What entry did you use?   _____

What is the OSI message numbered?   _____

Enter a received-from (Mr. Andrews) and end the PNR.

II.   Retrieve the PNR for passenger Ackerman and take the following actions, recording each entry as you go along.

Request a high fiber meal (HFML) on all flights.

_____

Inform the airline that Mr. Ackerman has a broken arm.

_____

Since Mr. Ackerman has a broken arm, he will not be able to carry all of his baggage. Arrange a meet and assist (MAAS) at both arrival cities.

_____

Display the AFAX messages. What entry did you use?   _____

What is the OSI message numbered?   _____

Enter a received-from (passenger) and end the PNR.

III.   Jason Simmons, age 7, will be flying from Toronto (Pearson Airport) to Halifax on July 1 to visit his grandparents for the summer. They will drive him back to Toronto at the end of August. Book him a flight in "Y" on Air Canada departing at any time. His telephone number in Toronto is 416 555-1111 and his grandparents' number in Halifax is 902 555-1212. Your travel agency number is 922-1234 in your hometown. His mother, Jean Simmons, is calling to make the reservation and will pick up the ticket documents this afternoon. Make the booking for Jason, creating a PNR with the mandatory fields, then use the "ER entry to end and re-retrieve the PNR.

What entry did you use to add the name field?

_____

Since Jason will be traveling unaccompanied, make the following additions to the PNR. Record each entry that you use.

Add an OSI to advise Air Canada that Jason's grandmother, Mrs. Mary Simmons, will meet Jason in Halifax.

_____

Order a child meal (CHML) for Jason.

_____

Add an SSR indicating that Jason is traveling unaccompanied.

_____

Enter a received-from field and end the PNR to save the changes you have made.

Format Review

OSI Messages

```
4OSI POLISH SPEAKER      Enter an AFAX OSI message into a PNR (for AA flights
                         only)

3OSI AC FIRST TIME FLYER
                         Enter a GFAX OSI message to AC

3OSI YY FIRST TIME FLYER
                         Enter a GFAX OSI message to all airlines
```

```
4OSI POLISH SPEAKER-1.2
```
Enter an AFAX OSI message into a PNR regarding passenger 1.2

```
3OSI AC FIRST TIME FLYER-1.2
```
Enter a GFAX OSI message to AC regarding passenger 1.2

SSR Messages

```
4MAAS2-1.1
```
Enter an AFAX SSR message requesting meet and assist (MAAS) service for passenger 1.1 on segment 2

```
3VLML4-1.1,2.1
```
Enter a GFAX SSR message requesting a vegetarian meal (VLML) for passengers 1.1 and 2.1 on segment 4

```
4NSML4,5-1.1,2.1
```
Enter an AFAX SSR message requesting a no-salt (NSML) meal for passengers 1.1 and 2.1 on segments 4 and 5

```
3UMNR/UM 08
```
Enter a GFAX message stating that the passenger is an 8-year-old unaccompanied minor

```
4UMNR/UM 08 09-1.1,2.1
```
Enter an AFAX message for multiple unaccompanied minors, passenger 1.1 is 8 years old and passenger 2.1 is 9 years old

```
3INFT/CHIU/SAMUEL MSTR/12APR14-1.2
```
Enter SSR message for a lap infant, specifying infant name (CHIU/SAMUEL MSTR), birthdate (12APR14) and the name item number of the adult on whose lap he will sit (-1.2)

Redisplay

```
*P3
```
Display the GFAX field of a PNR

```
*P4
```
Display the AFAX field of a PNR

TSA Secure Flight Documentation

`3DOCSA/P/US/55551111/US/03JUN73/M/05OCT14/SMITH/JOHN/IAN-1.1`

Enter secure flight documentation for passenger John Ian Smith (passenger 1.1) including optional passport information, for all airlines except AA (GFAX)

`4DOCSA/P/US/55551111/US/03JUN73/M/05OCT14/SMITH/JOHN/IAN-1.1`

As previous, but for airline AA only (AFAX)

`3DOCS/DB/03JUN73/M/SMITH/JOHN/IAN-1.1`

Enter secure flight documentation without passport information for passenger John Ian Smith (passenger 1.1) for all airlines except AA (GFAX)

`4DOCS/DB/03JUN73/M/SMITH/JOHN/IAN-1.1`

As previous, but for airline AA (AFAX)

`3DOCO//R/123456789-1.2`

Enter a Redress Number for passenger 1.2 for all airlines except AA (GFAX) (Use "K" for Known Traveler Number)

`4DOCO//R/123456789-1.2`

Enter a Redress Number for passenger 1.2 for airline AA (AFAX) (Use "K" for Known Traveler Number)

`*P4D`

Display AFAX security information

`*P3D`

Display GFAX security information

LEARNING OUTCOMES

At the end of this lesson, you should be able to:

• Change the information in a PNR field
• Delete an item in a PNR field
• Cancel a booked flight in a PNR
• Change a booked flight in a PNR
• Insert a new flight into a PNR
• Remove a passenger from a PNR (reduce a PNR)
• Divide a passenger from a PNR

This lesson teaches PNR management skills. After a PNR is built and ended (remember that "ending" a PNR stores it in the Sabre database), a passenger may call you with a change to her travel plans. After changing the flights in her itinerary, you may need to change the ticketing date. And, while talking to your client, you may find out that the PNR contains an incorrect phone number which should be changed as well.

The entries to change and delete PNR passenger data may appear difficult because they are long. However, they all follow the same format:

ICK *followed by* **PNR Item Nmbr (optional)** *followed by* ¤ *followed by* **New Data (optional)**

Itinerary modification entries are much simpler but very important. :wq Finding the best possible flight for a client initially, and when his travel plans change, is a critical service offered by travel professionals.

When several passengers are booked together in one PNR, they all share the same itinerary. If one or more of the passengers needs to cancel or change their trip, the PNR must be "reduced" or "divided". Reducing a PNR simply means removing one or more passengers from the reservation. Dividing a PNR means splitting the reservation into two different reservations.

Review Questions

Changing Passenger Data

1. What character is found in all passenger data change entries?

_____

2. When is an item number required in the entry to change or delete passenger data?

_____

```
  1.2TAYLOR/GARY MR/KATHERINE MRS
  1 DL4871Y 18AUG 5 JFKYYZ SS2  1525 1810 /DCDL /E
  2 DL4872Y 27AUG 7 YYZJFK SS2  1425 1655 /DCDL /E
TKT/TIME LIMIT
  1.TAW26JUN/
PHONES
  1.JFK212 565-2291-A
  2.JFK212 222-3333-H
  3.JFK212 229-2323-B
PASSENGER EMAIL DATA EXISTS   *PE TO DISPLAY ALL
A0A0.A0A0*AAB 1722/10JUL
```

The following four questions are based on the above partial Sabre PNR.

3. What entry changes the ticketing date to June 18?

_____

4. What entry changes the spelling of Katherine to Catherine?

_____

5. What entry changes the home phone number to 222-3334?

_____

6. What entry appends extension 1298 to the business telephone number, indicating that the number belongs to Gary?

_____

```
*PE
EMAIL ADDRESS
  1.¥GTAYLOR@AMHP.COM¥          1.1 TAYLOR/GARY MR
  2.¥KAT.TAY@MAC.COM¥           1.2 TAYLOR/KATHERINE MRS
```

The following question is based on the above Sabre display.

7. Gary would like to change his e-mail address from his work e-mail to his personal e-mail. What entry will change his e-mail to "GAR.TAY@MAC.COM"?

_____

```
*N
 1.3JOHNSON/WILLIAM MR/BRENDA MRS/ANNA MISS   2.1VANOWEN/JOANN MS
 3.2MEYERS/JOHN MR/JANICE MRS
```

The following question is based on the above Sabre name field.

8.   After you display the name field, you notice a few spelling errors. What entries make the following changes?

Johnson to Johnston _____

John and Janice Meyers to John and Janis Myers _____

_____

Joann to Joanne _____

Deleting Passenger Data

9.   The entry to delete passenger data is different than the entry to change passenger data in what respect?

_____

_____

```
1.1WILLIAMSON/ROD MR   2.1KIRKOV/ALEKSANDER MR
3.1GLASTONE/JOE MR
 1 DL 802Q 29NOV 1 SEALAX HK3   1500 1725 /DCDL*34400L /E
 2 DL 169Q 05DEC 7 LAXSEA HK3   1650 1905 /DCDL*34400L /E
TKT/TIME LIMIT
  1.TAW11NOV/
PHONES
  1.SEA206-343-9900-A
  2.SEA206-772-2442-B WILLIAMSON
  3.SEA206-222-1192-B GLASTONE
REMARKS
  1.BOOK HOTEL IN LAX
  2.BOOK CAR IN LAX
RECEIVED FROM - KIRKOV
A0A0.A0A0*AHK 1430/03NOV NEEVKK
```

The following three questions are based on the above Sabre PNR.

10. Mr. Glastone, who has resigned from his job, asks you to remove his business telephone number from the PNR. What entry would you make?

_____

11. What entry will delete the first remark?

_____

12. Assuming that you were in the process of reducing the party, what entry would delete Mr. Kirkov's name from the name field?

_____

Canceling Segments

```
1.2RUBENS/CORY MR/GEORGETTE MRS
 1 DL2147Y 03MAR 5 SEALAX SS2   1310 1534  /DCDL /E
 2 AA6118Y 05MAR 7 LAXSYD SS2   1300 2035  06MAR 1 /DCAA /E
 3 QF 505Y 07MAR 2 SYDASP SS2   0850 1135  /DCQF /E
 4 QF 546Y 10MAR 5 ASPSYD SS2   1510 1825  /DCQF /E
 5 AA6117Y 15MAR 3 SYDLAX SS2   1730 1400  /DCAA /E
 6 DL 169Y 20MAR 1 LAXSEA SS2   1650 1905  /DCDL /E
A0A0.A0A0*AAB 1752/10JAN
```

The following four questions are based on the above partial Sabre PNR. Treat each question as a separate transaction.

13. If your clients decide not to take the side trip from Sydney (SYD) to Alice Springs (ASP), what entry would cancel the applicable segments?

_____

14. Suppose the clients decide to drive from Seattle (SEA) to Los Angeles (LAX) and park their car at LAX while on holiday. What is the entry to cancel the segments between Seattle and Los Angeles?

_____

15. What entry cancels the unwanted segments if your clients decide to stay in Alice Springs (ASP) and not return to the United States?

_____

16. Suppose that your clients decide not to travel at all. What entry would cancel the entire itinerary?

_____

X3 NXT REPLACES 3

The following question is based on the above Sabre response.

17. Assume that you have just canceled segment 3 of a four-segment itinerary. What is the above response advising you?

_____

18. Suppose that Mr. Wayne has called to cancel his trip to Mexico City. List, in order, the entries you would make to retrieve the PNR, cancel the segments, save the change and end the PNR.

_____

Supplementary Entries

Canceling and Rebooking Itinerary Segments

In the online lesson, you learned how to cancel segments. Sometimes, instead of completely cancelling, your clients will want to modify their reservations, for example reschedule a flight or book in a different booking code. You cannot change data in a flight segment the same way you change data in other PNR fields. You can, however, cancel and rebook a flight at the same time. There are several entries that do this quickly and efficiently.

X1¥0023JUL
This entry is used to cancel a flight and rebook it for a different date. The flight number, number of seats booked and the booking code will all remain the same; only the date will change. Note that this entry is much more efficient than canceling the segment and then rebooking from availability or with a long sell entry. The entry is the standard segment cancellation entry followed by a Cross of Lorraine, two zeros and the new date.

X1¥01Y1
This entry is used to cancel a segment, replacing it with a flight booked from CPA. This entry is useful when you have booked the wrong flight, or your client decides

to take another flight and you still have the availability display in your work area. The entry is the segment cancellation entry followed by a Cross of Lorraine, and the book-from-availability entry.

WC1B

This entry will cancel a flight and rebook it in a different booking code. The flight number, number of seats booked and the date of travel will all remain the same; only the booking code will change. The entry consists of the action code "WC" for "want class", followed by the segment number and the new booking code.

WC1-4B

This is an expanded version of the last entry. It will rebook a range of segments in a new booking code. Note that the range is indicated by the first segment to be rebooked, a hyphen and the last segment to be rebooked.

WCAB

If the entire itinerary needs to be rebooked in a different booking code, the above entry may be used. In this case, the letter "A" is specified (for "All") instead of a segment or range of segments.

Segment Insertion

Sometimes you'll need to insert segments between existing segments in an already-booked itinerary. This might happen, for example, if your clients wish to add a side trip in the middle of their itinerary. Once an insert entry is made, the computer is in "insert mode" until the itinerary is redisplayed with the entry *I or *A.

/2

This is the standard "insert-after-segment" entry. It is used to place the computer in insert mode after segment 2. Segments booked after this entry are inserted in succession after segment 2. The computer will remain in insert mode until the entry *I or *A is made. The entry consists of the insert-after action code (/), followed by a segment number.

/Ø

This entry is used to insert before segment 1, or "after segment 0". It is usedI when your client needs to add a flight at the beginning of his itinerary.

/1A

This entry is used to insert an ARNK segment after the specified segment. In this example, an ARNK segment would be inserted into the itinerary after segment 1. This entry would be useful, for example, if you discovered that there was a break in your itinerary and you hadn't yet inserted an ARNK segment.

Exercises

Don't forget to sign in to the emulator before beginning the exercises, and to sign out after finishing the last problem.

I.   Display the PNR for Mr. and Mrs. Andersen. Jerome has called to make some changes to the reservation. Make the changes and record the entries you use.

The couple has decided not to travel to Nice. Cancel the applicable segments from Frankfurt to Nice and back.

_____

Change the home phone number to 234-3253. _____

Change the ticketing date to a week from today. _____

Change the last name to Anderson. _____

Enter a received-from (Mr. Anderson) and end the PNR to save the changes.

II.   Mr. Ronald Welsh has called to make a few changes to his reservation. Retrieve his PNR and make the following updates. Record each entry you use.

The clients have decided to depart one day earlier. Cancel and rebook the appropriate segment with one entry.

_____

The clients prefer to travel in economy class ("Y"). Make the single entry to cancel and rebook the entire itinerary in the new booking code.

_____

Change Porter's name to Peter.

_____

Receive the changes you have made and end the PNR to save these changes.

III. Display the PNR for passenger Ashlin. Mrs. Ashlin will be traveling with her husband and her seven-year-old son, Kent, to Los Angeles. She has requested some changes to their plans.

Mrs. Ashlin would like you to arrange a side trip to San Francisco for two days after her family arrives in Los Angeles. Using the insert-after entries, book three seats in "Y" on a United flight leaving around noon. The Ashlins would like to return to Los Angeles the day before they depart for home. Again, they would like to fly on United, leaving this time around 9:00 a.m.

What insert-after entries did you use? _____

What are the flight numbers of the segments you booked? Where do they appear in the itinerary?

_____

The PNR incorrectly gives Kent's age as six. Correct this mistake. What entry did you make?

_____

The Ashlins will no longer require a car in Los Angeles. Make the entry to cancel the remark. What entry did you make?

_____

Enter a received-from (Mrs. Ashlin) and end the PNR.

IV. George Caldwell has called to finalize arrangements for his business trip to Germany. Display his PNR and make the following changes.

Mr. Caldwell has decided to save money by traveling in economy class. Rebook the flights in "Y". What entry made this change?

_____

Mr. Caldwell would like to spend two nights in Frankfurt and then take the earliest morning flight to Munich. Add this flight, booked in "C", to the PNR. What flight did you book?

_____

George will be taking the train back to Frankfurt, so add an ARNK between Munich and Frankfurt. What entry did you use to add this surface segment?

_____

Since he will be visiting Munich, Mr. Caldwell may not return back to New York as scheduled. Change his confirmed flight from Frankfurt to an open return on Delta in "Y". Try to use a single entry. What entry did you use?

_____

George's company will be paying for the ticket. Change the form of payment to check. Don't forget to put a hyphen before the form of payment. What entry did you make?

_____

Enter a received-from and end the PNR to save these changes.

Format Review

Changing Passenger Data		
Changing Passenger Data	`91¤2Ø2 213-4444-A`	Change phone field item 1
	`-2¤SCHULTZ/MARIA MRS`	Change name item 2
	`7¤TAW23JUN/`	Change ticketing field (single item)
	`6¤MRS JONES`	Change the received-from field
	`51¤BOOK HERTZ CAR`	Change the first remark
	`PE1¤¥JKROWLENS@YAHOO.COM¥`	Change the first passenger e-mail address
	`32¤OSI UA SPEAKS FRENCH`	Change the second GFAX
	`43¤OSI VIP PASSENGER`	Change the third AFAX
Deleting Passenger Data	`93¤`	Delete phone field item number 3
	`-2¤`	Delete name item 2
	`7¤`	Delete ticketing date
	`6¤`	Delete the received-from field
	`51¤`	Delete the first remark
	`32¤`	Delete the second GFAX
	`43¤`	Delete the third AFAX
	`PE1¤`	Delete the first passenger e-mail
Canceling Segments	`X3`	Cancel segment 3 of an itinerary
	`X3/5/6`	Cancel segments 3, 5 and 6

	X2-5	Cancel segments 2 through 5
	XI	Cancel the entire itinerary
Rebooking Segments	WC1B	Rebook segment 1 in booking code "B"
	WC1-4B	Rebook segments 1 through 4 in booking code "B"
	WCAB	Rebook all segments in booking code "B"
Cancel and Rebook	X1¥0023JUL	Cancel segment 1 and rebook it for July 23
	X1¥01Y3	Cancel segment 1 and rebook it from availability
Segment Insertion	/2	Put computer in "insert mode" for insertion after segment 2
	/Ø	Put computer in "insert mode" for insertion before segment 1 (after segment 0)
	/2A	Insert an ARNK segment after segment 2
Reducing a Party	,2	Change the number of seats in an itinerary to 2
Dividing a Party	D2	Divide out name item 2
	D2*3	Divide out name items 2 and 3
	D2.2	Divide out name item 2.2
	F	File PNR

LEARNING OUTCOMES

At the end of this lesson, you should be able to:

•Assign seats by type
•Cancel a seat assignment

On the majority of flights, each passenger is assigned a specific seat on the airplane. The sooner the seat is assigned, the more likely the passenger will receive his preferred seat type. If you do not assign a seat, the airline will eventually assign one to the passenger, but it could end up being an undesirable middle seat.

Most passengers prefer either a window seat for a view, or an aisle seat for easy access to the lavatories (bathrooms). A window seat and an aisle seat are the two most common seat types. There are other characteristics which describe seat types, such as bulkhead, exit row, etc., which you will learn about in the next lesson. While the vast majority of flights (if not all flights) do not allow smoking, Sabre still distinguishes between smoking and non-smoking seats and an "s" may be included in your entry to assign seats in a smoking section.

Each seat on an aircraft is identified by a row number and seat letter; for example, 10A, 24F, etc.

Review Questions

Seat Assignment

1. When you specify a location code in the seat assignment entry, Sabre randomly selects seats for all passengers in the PNR according to the code. What codes are used to assign the following seat types?

    Window _____

    Aisle _____

    Front of plane _____

    Right side of plane _____

2. Let's assume that Mr. and Mrs. Chen are traveling on a direct flight from Los Angeles to Hong Kong. If you make the entry "4G1/W", seats are assigned for both passengers on segment 1. If Mr. Chen is assigned a window seat, where will Mrs. Chen sit?

    _____

3. What seat type is assigned with the entry "4G2/AL"?

    _____

```
1.1HUI/JOHN MR  2.1MAIER/TOM MR
 1 UA 206Y 07AUG 1 SFOYYZ SS2  1320 2100 /DCUA /E
 2 UA1105Y 30AUG 3 YYZSFO SS2  0950 1224 /DCUA /E
A0A0.A0A0*AAB 1850/10JUN
```

The following question is based on the above partial Sabre PNR.

4.   What entry assigns opposite aisle seats for Mr. Hui and Mr. Maier on both segments?

_____

```
1.2SIMMONS/WILLIAM MR/CAITLIN MRS
 1 AC 840Y 18FEB 5 YYZMAN SS2  2130 0915  19FEB 6 /DCAC /E
 2 AC 841Y 28FEB 1 MANYYZ SS2  1135 1410  /DCAC /E
A0A0.A0A0*AAB 1853/10JAN
```

The following question is based on the above partial Sabre PNR.

5.   What entry assigns an aisle seat, along with the adjacent seat, on both segments?

_____

```
DONE   SN 547C 05DEC BRUJFK N      REQUESTED TYLER/ANNA MS
22J    AA1165Y 08DEC JFKMIA N                TYLER/ANNA MS
27J    AA  98Y 11DEC MIAJFK N                TYLER/ANNA MS
DONE   SN 534C 14DEC JFKBRU N      REQUESTED TYLER/ANNA MS
```

The following four questions are based on the above Sabre seat assignment response.

6.   What does the word "DONE" mean? _____

_____

7.   In what seat will Ms. Tyler be sitting from JFK to MIA? _____

8.   In what seat will Ms. Tyler be sitting from MIA back to JFK? _____

9.   Why can't you tell which seats have been assigned for the other segments?

_____

_____

```
1.1TYLER/ANNA MS
 1 SN 547C 05DEC 1 BRUJFK HK1    0730 2125 HRQ /ABSN*SFG56T /E
 2 AA1165Y 08DEC 4 JFKMIA HK1    0930 1230 HRS /DCAA*3127YY /E
 3 AA   98Y 11DEC 7 MIAJFK HK1   1345 1644 HRS /DCAA*3127YY /E
 4 SN 534C 14DEC 3 JFKBRU HK1    1945 0825 15DEC 4 HRQ /ABSN*SFG56T /E
```

The following four questions are based on the above partial Sabre PNR.

10.   Which letters indicate that seats have been requested but have not yet been confirmed?

_____

11.   Which letters indicate that seats have been confirmed? _____

12.   What entry displays the assigned seats? _____

13.   What entry cancels all the seat assignments for this PNR? _____

Exercises

Don't forget to sign in to the emulator before beginning the exercises, and to sign out after finishing the last problem.

I.   Display the PNR for passenger Starcher. Assign a window seat for all segments.

What entry did you make?   _____

What seat has been assigned for the British Airways flight?   _____

Redisplay the PNR. How can you tell that specific seats have been reserved?

_____

Display the seat data. What entry did you use?   _____

Now cancel all the seats. What entry did you use?   _____

Ignore the transaction.

II.   Display the PNR for passenger Hartwell. Assign an aisle seat and adjacent seats for segment 2 only.

What entry did you make? _____

What seat has been assigned to Master Jake? _____

Now cancel these seat assignments. What entry did you make?

_____

Ignore the transaction.

Format Review

Seat Assignment	4G1/W	Assign window (W) and adjacent seats for all passengers on segment 1
	4G1,2,3/A	Assign aisle (A) and adjacent seats for all passengers on segments 1, 2 and 3
	4GA/W	Assign window (W) and adjacent seats for all passengers on all segments
Seat Assignment Display	*B	Display all assigned seats in a PNR
Canceling Seat Assignments	4GX1	Cancel all reserved seats for segment 1
	4GX1,2	Cancel all reserved seats for segments 1 and 2
	4GXALL	Cancel all reserved seats for all segments

LEARNING OUTCOMES

At the end of this lesson, you should be able to:

•**Display a seat map**
•**Read a seat map**
•**Assign seats by seat number**
•**Identify paid seating on a seat map**

The ability to read seat maps is a critical skill for the travel professional. While cryptic, the seat maps in a GDS provide detailed information on the configuration of the aircraft by showing the location of lavatories (bathrooms), the galley (kitchen), bulkhead seats, airplane wings and exit rows. Many maps provide additional information on a seat's characteristics as well. This level of information is rarely available when booking flights on an Internet booking site, such as those operated by the airline or an online travel agency.

Many passengers have strong preferences as to where they want to sit on an airplane. When you choose a seat from a seat map, you will be able to reserve the best available seat for your client.

Review Questions

Seat Maps and Specific Seat Assignment

```
1.2SNODGRASS/FELIX MR/VICTORIA MRS
 1 AC 148Y 20JUN 2 YVRYYZ SS2  1200 1916 /DCAC /E
 2 AC 115Y 27JUN 2 YYZYVR SS2  1700 1850 /DCAC /E
AØAØ.AØAØ*AAB 1125/12MAR
```

The following two questions are based on the above partial Sabre PNR.

1. What entry displays a seat map for Air Canada 148 so that you can select exact seat numbers for your clients?

    _____

2. Is there a single Sabre entry that displays seat maps for both segments?

    _____

```
AUTH-126   320
   1 - SFO  2 - ORD
   NO SMOKING FLIGHT
        A   B   C       D   E   F
 W 9    .   .   .       .   .   .       9 W
 W10    .   .   .       *   *   *      10W
 W11X   .   .   .       .   .   .      X11W
 W12X   .   .   .       .   .   .      X12W
 W13    .   .   .       .   .   .      13W
 W14    .   .   .       .   .   .      14W
 W15    .   .   .       *   *   .      15W
 W16    .   .   .       *   *   .      16W
  17    .   .   .       .   .   .      17
 AVAIL NO SMK:  *     BLOCK  :  /  LEAST PREF: U    BULKHEAD: BHD
  AVAIL SMKING: -     PREMIUM: Q  UPPER DECK: J   EXIT ROW:  X
  SEAT TAKEN: .  WING: W  PAID : P  LAVATORY: LAV GALLEY: GAL
  PREF ACCESS LAV: PAL  DOOR: DOR     SCREEN: SCR    CLOSET: CLS
  PREF ACCESS : H   BASSINET: B       UMNR: M    REARFACE:
```

The following eight questions are based on the above partial United Airlines seat map.

3. Why would you not assign seats in rows 11 and 12 to child, elderly or disabled passengers?

   _____

4. What entry assigns the available aisle seat in row 15 for segment 1?

   _____

5. What does the letter "W" indicate about the seats in the seat map display?

   _____

6. If you were assigning seats for three passengers who asked to sit together, for segment 1, what entry would you make?

   _____

7. Note the "¥" in the lower-right corner. This indicates that there is more of the map to see. What entry scrolls down the map?

   _____

8. Sometimes an airline will reserve certain seats in the coach/economy cabin for passengers who have paid the highest fares or for those who have

frequent-flyer memberships. What letter on a United Airlines seat map would indicate that a "premium" seat can only be assigned for these passengers? Refer to the legend for your answer.

_____

9. If a passenger is traveling with a three-month-old infant, you should look for a seat identified by the letter . . .

_____

10. Suppose you have a client who walks with a cane and has difficulty getting into and out of airline seats. For passengers with mobility difficulties, airlines usually offer seats with movable armrests for easier access. What letter identifies these preferred access seats on a United Airlines seat map?

_____

```
AC RESPONSE
    20 A   B   C      D   E   F   20
    21 A   B   C      D   E   F   21
    22 A   B   C      D   E   F   22
    23 A   B   C      D   E   F   23
    24 A   B   C      DVQ E   F   24
    25 A   B   C      DVQ E   F   25
    26 A   B   C      D   E   F   26
    27 .P  .P  .P     DVQ .P  .P  27
    28 .P  .P  .P     DVQ .P  .P  28
    29 .PV .PV .PV    .PV .PV .PV 29
        TOILET   GALLEY   TOILET
        DOOR              DOOR
- - - - - - - - - - - - - - - - - - - - - - - - - - -
LEGEND-SEAT CHARACTERISTICS
        .     SEAT OCCUPIED/UNAVAILABLE TO PASSENGER
        P     SEAT PROTECTED FOR AIRPORT
        G     SEAT DESIGNATED TO Y/M/SUPER ELITE/ELITE/PRESTIGE
        V     NON PREFERRED SEAT - SELECT LAST
        Q     LIFTABLE ARMREST SEAT
        B     BASSINET SEAT
        L     BULKHEAD
      -ROW CHARACTERISTICS
        W     WING
¥
*MD TO SEE MORE
```

The following three questions are based on the above partial Air Canada seat map.

11. What appears as the first code if the seat is available?

_____

12. Your client wants an aisle seat in the rear of the plane. What seat would you assign? Is this seat in the last three rows? If not, why?

_____

_____

13. The "¥" in the lower-left corner indicates that there is more of this display to view. What entry scrolls down?

_____

```
AUTH- 30    767
   1 - BOS  2 - LHR
   NO SMOKING FLIGHT
      A   B       D   G       H   J
      BHD BHD     BHD BHD     BHD BHD
    7 *   *       *   *       *   *    7
    8 .   .       *   *       *   .    8
    9 .   .       *   *       .   .    9
   10 *   *       *   *       *   *   10
   AVAIL NO SMK: *     BLOCK  : /  LEAST PREF: U    BULKHEAD: BHD
   AVAIL SMKING: -    PREMIUM: Q  UPPER DECK: J    EXIT ROW:  X
   SEAT TAKEN: .  WING: W PAID : P  LAVATORY: LAV GALLEY: GAL
   PREF ACCESS LAV: PAL  DOOR: DOR    SCREEN: SCR   CLOSET: CLS
```

The following three questions are based on the above partial American Airlines seat map.

14. This seat map is for travel between what two cities?

_____

15. This seat map is for what aircraft type?

_____

16. What does the code "BHD" stand for and what does this mean?

_____

_____

```
AUTH-332    H44
   1 - LAX   2 - LHR
   NO SMOKING FLIGHT
      A    B    C       D    E    F    G       H    J    K
      BHD  BHD
  16  .    .    .                                             16
  17  .    .    .       GAL  GAL  GAL          BHD       BHD   17
  18  .    .    .       BHD       BHD  BHD     .    .    .     18
 W19  .    .    .       .    .    .    .       .    .    .     19W
 W20  .    .    .       .    .    .    .       .    .    .     20W
 W21  .    .    .       .    .    .    .       .    .    .     21W
 W22  .    .    .       .    .    .    .       .    .    .     22W
 W23  .    .    .       .    .    .    .       .    .    .     23W
 W24  .    .    .       .    .    .    .       .    .    .     24W
 W25  .    .    .       .    .    .    *       .    .    .     25W
 W26  LAV  LAV          *    *    .    .       .    *    *     26W
 W27                    *    .    .    .                      27W
 W28X .    .            .    .    .    .       .    .        X28W
 W29  .    .    .       .    .    .    .       .    .    .     29W ¥
```

The following four questions are based on the above partial British Airways seat map.

17. Your two clients wish to sit next to each other, with one aisle seat. What entry would you make to assign the seats for segment 1?

_____

18. Now suppose you have two clients who wish to sit next to each other, with one window seat. What seat assignment entry would you make for segment 1?

_____

19. Your three clients wish to sit as close to each other as possible. What is the best seat assignment entry to make for segment 1?

_____

20. Which row is an exit row?

_____

21. What code in a standard seat map indicates an Air Extras seat?

_____

Exercises

Don't forget to sign in to the emulator before beginning the exercises, and to sign out after finishing the last problem.

I. Retrieve the PNR for passenger Peacock and display a seat map for segment one.

What entry did you make? _____

The passengers would like a window seat and adjacent seats as far front in the plane as possible. They don't want an exit row, however. What seats would you recommend?

_____

Make the entry to assign appropriate seats for these passengers. What entry did you make?

_____

Try booking these same seats for segment two. What entry did you make?

_____

Were the seats available? _____

Display the seat data. Who has the window seat? _____

Enter a received-from (Ms. Peacock) and end the transaction.

II. Retrieve the PNR for passenger Samour and display a seat map for segment one. The passenger would like a window seat that is not behind a bulkhead,

as far in the front of the plane as possible. Make the entry to assign the appropriate seat.

What entry did you make? _____

Display the seat map again and make the entry to move down.

What entry did you make? _____

What letter indicates a restricted row or seat? _____

Display the seat assignment, and then, without displaying a seat map, make the entry to assign the same seat for segment two. What entry did you make?

_____

Enter a received-from (passenger) and end and retrieve the PNR in one entry. Make the entry to display the seat assignments. Was the same seat available for segment two, or was a different seat assigned?

_____

Ignore the transaction.

III.   Retrieve the PNR for passenger Bagwell and display a seat map for segment two. These passengers all want a window seat, and don't mind that they won't be sitting together. They also want to sit as far front in the plane as possible. Assign appropriate seats.

What entry did you make? _____

The passengers might be changing their outbound plans, so they don't require seats for segment one at this time. Enter a received-from (Paul) and end the transaction.

Format Review

Seat Maps	`4G1*`	Display a seat map for the flight in segment 1
	`¤MD`	Move down a seat map from AC
Specific Seat Assignment	`4G1/26A`	Assign seat 26A on segment 1
	`4GA/26A`	Assign seat 26A on all segments
	`4G3/16DEF`	Assign seats 16D, 16E and 16F on segment 3
	`4G2/25A26AB`	Assign seats 25A, 26A and 26B on segment 2

LEARNING OUTCOMES

At the end of this lesson, you should be able to:

• **Interpret vehicle type codes**
• **Display car availability**
• **Book a rental car**
• **Read a rental car reservation in a PNR**
• **Add optional modifiers to the car sell entry**

Booking rental cars is another service the travel agent can offer a client. In fact, most business travelers will expect their travel agent to book ground services (car, hotel, limousine, etc.). Rental car bookings can be an excellent source of commission revenue.

There is a wealth of rental car data stored in the Sabre Cars Plus System. While this information is more cryptic than what you will see in a car company's online booking tool, it is faster to access and will allow you to shop rates between car firms. Corporate discounts, promotions and rates can all be booked through Sabre.

Another advantage of using the Sabre Cars Plus System is that your client's booking will be stored in his PNR. If a passenger has a question about his booking, all you have to do is retrieve his PNR to see the reservation (as opposed to calling the car company).

Most rental cars are required at an airport, which means you can use flight information in the PNR to quickly display car availability for the correct city and dates. Likewise, the renter's name will be read from the PNR name field when you book the car, and will be sent to the car company with the booking. These types of shortcuts make using the GDS the fastest and most efficient method of booking rental cars.

Review Questions

Vendor and Vehicle Type Codes

1. In Lesson 2, you learned how to decode and encode car companies or "vendors". For review, what entry . . .

   Encodes the car rental company Payless? _____

   Decodes the car vendor code "ZR"? _____

2. What vehicle type code represents a luxury four-door car with manual transmission and air conditioning?

   _____

3. What car types do each of the following codes represent?

   CC _____

   *V _____

   FCAR _____

CTMN _____

AFWD _____

Shopper's Car Quote

4. A shopper's car quote displays only the . . .

_____

```
1.2GOSSELIN/DANIEL MR/JOCELYN MRS
 1 AA 344Y 26MAY 2 YVRDFW HK2  0715 1315 /DCAA*UMBEBZ /E
 2 AA1437Y 30MAY 6 DFWYVR HK2  1849 2109 /DCAA*UMBEBZ /E
TKT/TIME LIMIT
  1.TAW07MAY/
PHONES
  1.YVR604-923-1732-A
  2.YVR604-474-0123-H
RECEIVED FROM - MRS
Y2VS.Y2VS*AKH 0200/06MAY UMBEBZ
```

The following two questions are based on the above Sabre PNR.

5. List the specific details that Sabre reads from the air segments to display a shopper's car quote for the clients' stay in Dallas (DFW).

_____

_____

6. What entry will request a shopper's car quote for the full duration of the stay?

_____

```
DALLAS                         16MAR MON  2005
                               20MAR FRI  1720  RENTAL   3DAYS 21HRS
--------------------------------------------------------------------
                     R C USD RATE/PLAN MI/KM   CHG        APPROX C
  1 ET ENTERPRI ECMR         22.01D    UNL     .00        101.23 O
  2 AL ALAMO    ECAR         23.23D    UNL     .00        106.85 O
  3 ZR DOLLAR   ECAR         23.23D    UNL     .00        106.85 O
  4 ZI AVIS     ECAR         24.45D    UNL     .00        112.48 O
  5 ZT THRIFTY  ECAR         28.12D    UNL     .00        129.36 I
  6 ZL NATIONAL ECAR         35.46D    UNL     .00        163.12 I
  7 ZD BUDGET   ECAR         35.46D    UNL     .00        163.12 I
  8 AC ACE RENT ECAR         35.46D    UNL     .00        163.12 O
  9 ZE HERTZ    ECAR         39.13D    UNL     .00        180.00 I
--------------------------------------------------------------------
ALL TOTAL PRICES ARE RETURNED DIRECT CONNECT FROM CAR ASSOCIATE
* BEST PUBLICLY AVAILABLE RATE
C  COMMISSION FX FIXED     05 PERCENTAGE     BLANK-COMM UNKNOWN
R  RATE AND/OR VEHICLE ON REQUEST     CURRENCY CONVERTED
-  AMOUNT TOO LARGE                   C CONTRACT RATE
L  INCLUSIVE RATE                     ? PLAN CHANGED BY ASSOCIATE
C  RENTAL LOC INFO
I-IN TERMINAL                    R-IN TERMINAL/RENTAL SHUTTLE
A-ON AIRPORT/AIRPORT SHUTTLE      S-ON AIRPORT/RENTAL SHUTTLE
```

The following five questions are based on the above partial Sabre shopper's car quote.

7.   How many rental companies are located within the airport terminal? Record their two-letter company codes.

_____

8.   What is the rate type and how can you tell? (daily, weekend, weekly, monthly)

_____

9.   The "Approx" column shows the approximate cost of the car rental for the entire rental period. How long is this rental period?

_____

10. Your client, Mr. Gonzalez, is interested in booking the least expensive car rental. He doesn't plan to drive any farther than 80 miles per day. Which company offers the best rate and what is the rental cost? Be specific with your explanation and include all possible charges.

_____

_____

11. What is different about the Enterprise vehicle type compared to the other vehicles listed?

_____

```
1.2WILLOWS/JAMES MR/JAYNE MRS
 1 UA 863Y 10FEB 4 SFOSYD SS2  2255 0630  12FEB 6 /DCUA /E
 2 QF 416Y 14FEB 1 SYDCNS SS2  1020 1320 /DCQF /E
 3 QF 943Y 17FEB 4 CNSASP SS2  1520 1730 /DCQF /E
 4 QF 492Y 25FEB 5 ASPMEL SS2  1725 2130 /DCQF /E
 5 UA4920Y 28FEB 1 MELSYD SS2  0820 0935 /DCUA /E
 6 UA 862Y 28FEB 1 SYDSFO SS2  1100 0720 /DCUA /E
TKT/TIME LIMIT
  1.TAW03FEB/                                             ¥
```

The following five questions are based on the above partial Sabre PNR.

12. What entry displays a shopper's car quote for Avis (ZI) and Budget (ZD) for the passengers' first stay in Sydney (SYD)?

_____

13. What is the best entry to display a shopper's car quote for economy (E) cars (C) with automatic transmission (A) and air conditioning (R) for the clients' stay in Cairns (CNS)?

_____

14. What entry displays a shopper's car quote with Thrifty (ZT) and Dollar (ZR) for ICARs and SCARs for the clients' stay in Alice Springs (ASP)?

_____

15. When you make the entry to display a shopper's car quote for the full stay in Alice Springs (ASP), will daily or weekly rates be displayed? Explain your answer.

_____

_____

16. For their last stop on the itinerary, James and Jayne would like either a premium (P) or luxury (L) vehicle. What entry requests a shopper's car quote for all premium- and luxury-sized cars?

_____

```
*I
 1 AC 930V 07DEC 2 YULMIA HK5  0850 1215 /DCAC*BIEU33 /E
 2 AC 933V 17DEC 5 MIAYUL HK5  1310 1630 /DCAC*BIEU33 /E
```

The following question is based on the above Sabre itinerary.

17. What entry requests a shopper's quote for pick-up at the time and destination of segment 1, with drop-off on December 16 at 5:00 p.m.?

_____

18. Suppose you have a client who wants to know how much it will cost to rent a car in Montreal (YUL) for the weekend.. What entry displays a shopper's car quote for a rental from 5:00 p.m. this Friday to 9:00 p.m. this Sunday?

_____

19. After you quote a rate for your client, you make other entries and the car quote is removed from the screen. If your client has additional questions on the rental, what entry can you make to redisplay the shopper's car quote?

_____

Single-Company Car Quote

20. What vehicle types are displayed in the single-company car quote?

_____

```
*I
 1 AA  55V 02DEC 4 MANORD HK1  1020 1235    /DCAA*ZQPQRM /E
 2 AA  54V 09DEC 4 ORDMAN HK1  1810 0740 10DEC 5 /DCAA*ZQPQRM /E
```

The following question is based on the above Sabre itinerary.

21. What entry requests a single-company car quote for Enterprise (ET) for the passenger's stay in Chicago (ORD)?

_____

22. What entry redisplays a single-company car quote if it is removed from your screen?

_____

23. What entry displays a single-company car quote for Dollar (ZR) in San Francisco (SFO) for pick-up at 8:00 a.m. on August 11th and drop-off at 4:00 p.m. on August 25th?

_____

Booking a Car

```
ZR DOLLAR                    *RATES RETURNED VIA DIRECT CONNECT
SAN FRANCISCO                 IN TERMINAL      OPEN 0000-2359
                              11AUG MON  0800  CORPORATE LOCATION
                              25AUG MON  1600  RENTAL  14DAYS  8HRS
-------------------------------------------------------------------
         R C USD RATE/PLAN      MI      CHG                  APPROX
  1 ECAR          152.99W       UNL     .00                  390.97
  2 CCAR          175.99W       UNL     .00                  449.62
  3 ICAR          197.99W       UNL     .00                  505.97
  4 SCAR          211.99W       UNL     .00                  541.62
  5 FCAR          224.99W       UNL     .00                  574.97
  6 LCAR          238.99W       UNL     .00                  610.62
-------------------------------------------------------------------
ALL TOTAL PRICES ARE RETURNED DIRECT CONNECT FROM CAR ASSOCIATE
* BEST PUBLICLY AVAILABLE RATE
C  COMMISSION  FX FIXED     05 PERCENTAGE    BLANK-COMM UNKNOWN
R  RATE AND/OR VEHICLE ON REQUEST           # CURRENCY CONVERTED
-  AMOUNT TOO LARGE                         C CONTRACT RATE
L  INCLUSIVE RATE
G  GUARANTEE  REQUIRED - CREDIT CARD MANDATORY AT TIME OF SELL
P  PREPAYMENT REQUIRED - CREDIT CARD MANDATORY AT TIME OF SELL
PLAN  D-DAILY  E-WEEKEND  W-WEEKLY  M-MONTHLY  B-BUNDLED
-------------------------------------------------------------------
```

The following question is based on the above partial Sabre single company car quote.

24. What entry books the intermediate sized car?

_____

Supplementary Entries

Single Company Car Quote from Shopper's Car Quote

Shopper's car quote displays list only the least expensive vehicle for each car vendor. There may be times when you have a shopper's car quote on your screen, and you would like to see the other vehicles offered by one of the companies listed. You may move from a shopper's car quote to a single-company car quote with the following entry.

```
CF*5
```
This entry displays a single-company car quote for the company listed on line 5 of a shopper's quote. The resulting quote would display all vehicles in order from smallest to largest. The entry is the shopper's car quote action code "CF", an asterisk and the line number of the company for which you want a single-company car quote.

Car Sell with Optional Modifiers

There will be times when your client may require non-standard service from a car rental company. For example, your client may require an infant car seat. Other times, you may need to inform the car rental company of your client's frequent flyer number, in order to redeem miles. You may transmit information and requests like this to the car company by appending modifiers to the end of the car sell entry.

```
ØC1/SI-RQST RED CAR
```
This is a car sell entry with the special information (SI) modifier. Like all modifiers, it is added to the end of the car sell entry, preceded with a slash (/). Following the slash is the two-letter identification code (SI), a hyphen and a free text field, in which a request for a red car has been entered. In application, this entry would book the car on line 1 of a car quote, adding a request for a red car.

All of the optional modifiers follow the same basic format. They are added to the end of the basic sell entry and consist of a slash followed by a one-, two- or three-letter code. Free text is entered after the code, and is usually separated from the code by a hyphen. Multiple modifiers may be specified in one car sell entry. Some of the more commonly used modifiers are shown below.

/ARR-	Arrival information (if not in PNR)	/CD-	Corporate ID number
/DO-	Drop-off location (if different than pick-up location)	/FT-	Frequent traveler/flyer number
		/G	Guarantee information
/ID-	Customer ID number	/NM-	Customer's name (if different than first name in PNR)
/RC-	Rate code		
/SI-	Special information	/SQ-	Special equipment (such as ski rack, child seat, car phone)
/W-	Request written confirmation		

Exercises

Don't forget to sign in to the emulator before beginning the exercises, and to sign out after finishing the last problem. Use the car encode/decode entries taught in Lesson 2 where necessary.

I. Display the PNR for passenger Abbott. Retrieve a shopper's quote for the passengers' entire stay in Honolulu. What entry did you make?

_____

Which vendor's rental location is located off terminal?

_____

Make the entry to move to a single-company car quote for Hertz. What entry did you make?

_____

What is the least expensive rate for a Hertz luxury car?

_____

Ignore this PNR.

II. Make the entry to display the PNR for passenger Barrows.

Retrieve a shopper's car quote for the passengers' entire stay in Seattle, for companies Thrifty, Enterprise and Alamo only. What entry did you make?

_____

What vehicle type was displayed for Enterprise?

_____

Make the entry to book the car from Alamo. What entry did you make?

_____

What is the weekly rate and rate for extra days?

_____

Enter a received-from (Mr. Barrows) and end the transaction.

III.　Retrieve the PNR for passenger Bennett.

Display a single-company car quote for Thrifty for ECARs only for the passengers' stay in Montreal. What entry did you make?

_____

How many free miles or kilometers are allowed for this car and what is the extra charge for additional miles or kilometers?

_____

Book this car, using two modifiers to record the following: A special information request for a Ford model and the Air Canada Aeroplan frequent-flyer number 151203709. If your entry is not accepted, read the error message and adjust the order in which you specify the two modifiers. What entry did you make that was accepted by the Sabre emulator?

_____

What is the confirmation number for the booking?

_____

Enter a received-from (Mrs. Bennett) and end the transaction.

IV.　Make the entry to display a single-company car quote for Budget in London (LHR) beginning two weeks from Monday for eight days, picking up at 3:00 p.m. and dropping off at 4:00 p.m.

What entry did you make?

_____

What is the least expensive vehicle type listed? Describe this vehicle.

_____

Sell the least expensive ICMN available. In what currency are the rates listed in the sell response?

_____

Now redisplay the last single-company car quote. In what currency were the rates originally quoted?

_____

Ignore this transaction.

V. Your clients would like to book an intermediate car in Vancouver for seven days beginning two weeks from Wednesday, picking up and returning the vehicle around noon. What car quote entry did you make?

_____

What company(ies) offer(s) them the least expensive rate?

_____

Ignore this partial transaction.

Format Review

Shopper's Car Quote	`CF1/2`	Display shopper's car quote for the airport, date, and time of segment 1, for return on the date and time of segment 2
	`CF1/2/CCAR`	Display shopper's car quote listing CCARs only
	`CF1/2/CC,IC`	Display shopper's car quote listing CCs and ICs
	`CF1/2-ZE,ZI,ZL`	Display shopper's car quote for ZE, ZI and ZL only
	`CF1/2/SCAR,ICAR-ZD,ZA`	Display shopper's car quote listing SCARs and ICARs from ZD and ZA

CF1-03JUL-9A	Display a shopper's car quote for the airport, date and time of segment 1, specifying return on July 3 at 9:00 a.m.
CFSFO/27MAR-29MAR/1600-0700	Display shopper's car quote at SFO for a rental from March 27 at 16.00 to March 29 at 07.00
CF*	Redisplay the last shopper's car quote display
CF*5	Display a single-company car quote for the company listed on line 5 of shopper's car quote

Single-Company Car Quote

CQ1/2ZI	Display a car quote for rental company ZI for the airport, date and time of segment 1, for return on the date and time of segment 2
CQ1/2ZI/CCAR	As previous, except listing CCARs only
CQ1ZI-03JUL-9A	Display a car quote for rental company ZI for the airport, date, and time of segment 1, specifying return on July 3 at 9:00 a.m.
CQECGVA/7MAY-9MAY/1200-1700	Display car quote at GVA for rental company EC for a rental from May 7 at 12.00 to May 9 at 17.00
CQ*	Redisplay last single-company car quote display

Car Sell

0C4	Book the car on line 4 of a car quote display
0C4¥2	Book 2 cars from line 4 of a car quote display
0C2/GAX37318929881125EXP11 17-SMITH	Book the car on line 2 of a car quote, with a guarantee to a credit card

```
ØC2/FT-AC12345567/SI-RQST CAMRY
```
Book the car on line 2 of a car quote, specifying the passenger's frequent flyer number (airline code precedes number) and including a special request. Note that the SI field must come last when using multiple modifiers.

```
X2
```
Cancel car segment number 2

Vehicle Type Matrix

M	Mini	C	Car	A	Automatic	R	Air Cond.
E	Economy	B	Car (2 Door)	M	Manual	N	No Air Cond.
C	Compact	D	Car (4 Door)				
I	Intermediate	W	Wagon				
S	Standard	V	Van				
F	Full-size	L	Limousine				
P	Premium	R	Recreation Vehicle				
L	Luxury	T	Convertible				
X	Special	S	Sports Car				
*	All	F	4-wheel Drive				
		X	Special				
		P	Pickup				
		J	All Terrain Vehicle				
		K	Truck				

Pseudo Vehicle Types

ACAR	All 2 or 4 door cars	AWGN	All station wagons
ATDR	All 2 door cars	AVAN	All vans
AFDR	All 4 door cars	AFWD	All 4 wheel drives
ASPC	All special vehicles	ATRV	All all-terrain vehicles
ASPT	All sports cars	APUP	All pickups
ACNV	All convertibles	ALMO	All limos
ACMN	All 2 or 4 door cars with manual transmission, no air conditioning	AREC	All recreational vehicles
		ATRK	All trucks (including pickups)

LEARNING OUTCOMES

At the end of this lesson, you should be able to:

- **"Dig Up" car information**
- **Read car rules**
- **Retrieve car policy displays**
- **Display a car vendor list**

This lesson teaches entries you can make in Sabre to retrieve information about car companies, rental locations, vehicle types and other car rental options and services. While these entries are not required to make a car booking, they will help you find information and answer questions your clients may have concerning their car rentals.

In this workbook lesson, you will be introduced to an entry that is used to display a list of all vendors (car companies) serving a particular airport.

Review Questions

Car Information Displays

1. What is the entry to display a list of car vendors and their codes?

    _____

2. What entry would you make if you wished to decode the vehicle type code ECMN?

    _____

3. What entry would you make if your client requests a toddler car seat for his rental car and you don't know the code to use in the "SQ-" modifier?

    _____

Car Rules

4. Car rules may be displayed from . . .

    _____

```
LOS ANGELES                  21MAY WED  1519
                             28MAY WED  1219  RENTAL   6DAYS 21HRS
- - - - - - - - - - - - - - - - - - - - - - - - - - - - - - - - - - - - - - -
                    R C USD RATE/PLAN MI/KM    CHG        APPROX C
   1 ZD BUDGET     ECAR         80.99W   UNL    .00         93.14 I
   2 FX FOX RENT   ECAR         87.99W   UNL    .00        101.19 O
   3 ET ENTERPRI   ECAR         89.99W   UNL    .00        103.49 O
   4 MW MIDWAY     ECMR         89.99W   UNL    .00        103.49 O
   5 ZA PAYLESS    ECAR         98.99W   UNL    .00        113.84 O
   6 ZR DOLLAR     ECAR        121.99W   UNL    .00        140.29 I
   7 ZT THRIFTY    ECAR        134.99W   UNL    .00        155.24 O
   8 ZL NATIONAL   ECAR        143.99W   UNL    .00        165.59 I
   9 AC ACE RENT   ECAR        144.99W   UNL    .00        166.74 I
  10 ZI AVIS       LCAR        229.99W   UNL    .00        264.49 I
  11 ZE HERTZ      ECAR        256.99W   UNL    .00        295.54 I
- - - - - - - - - - - - - - - - - - - - - - - - - - - - - - - - - - - - - - -
ALL TOTAL PRICES ARE RETURNED DIRECT CONNECT FROM CAR ASSOCIATE
* BEST PUBLICLY AVAILABLE RATE
C  COMMISSION  FX FIXED     05 PERCENTAGE     BLANK-COMM UNKNOWN
R  RATE AND/OR VEHICLE ON REQUEST      CURRENCY CONVERTED
-  AMOUNT TOO LARGE                    C CONTRACT RATE
L  INCLUSIVE RATE                      ? PLAN CHANGED BY ASSOCIATE
C  RENTAL LOC INFO
```

The following question is based on the above partial Sabre shopper's car quote.

5.   What entry displays car rules for the ECAR from Payless?

_____

```
ZA-PAYLESS        LOS ANGELES      OFF-SHUTTLE PROVIDED TO COUNTER
LAX  MCARØ
DATE OF PUP    - 18JUN, SUN
DATE OF RET    - 25JUN, SUN
RATE PLAN      - WY
PLAN MIN DAYS  - 4   PLAN MAX DAYS - 7   MAX RENTAL DAYS - 28
- - - - - - - - - - - - - - - - - - - - - - - - - - - - - - - - - - - - - -
DISPLAYED CURRENCY USD                   MILES      CHARGE/MI
RATE                          172.59      UNL
XTRA DAY                       25.79      UNL
XTRA HOUR                      12.79      UNL
- - - - - - - - - - - - - - - - - - - - - - - - - - - - - - - - - - - - - -
RATE CODE      - GENW
       GENERAL WEEKLY RATE
                                    GUAR RATE IS FOR 365 DAYS
FROM BOOKING DATE                                           ¥
```

The following two questions are based on the above Sabre car rule.

6.   The USD 172.59 rate is valid for up to how many days?

_____

7.   If the client returns the car on June 26, what is the additional charge?

_____

8.   How would you display the rules for the car on line 4 of a single-company car quote display?

_____

Corporate Policy

9.   What is the difference between corporate policy and local policy?

_____

_____

10. What entry displays the corporate policy for Dollar Rent A Car (ZR)?

_____

Local Policy

11. What entry displays a local policy for Budget (ZD) in Manchester (MAN)?

_____

```
ZD BUDGET                *RATES RETURNED VIA DIRECT CONNECT
MIAMI                     IN TERMINAL      OPEN 0000-2359
                          12JUN THU  1712  CORPORATE LOCATION
                          18JUN WED  1317  RENTAL    5DAYS 20HRS
      ------------------------------------------------------------
          R C USD RATE/PLAN    MI     CHG              APPROX
       1 ECAR        85.99W    UNL    .00               98.89
       2 CCAR        90.99W    UNL    .00              104.64
       3 ICAR       117.99W    UNL    .00              135.69
       4 SCAR       112.99W    UNL    .00              129.94
       5 FCAR       130.99W    UNL    .00              150.64
```

The following question is based on the above Sabre single-company car quote.

12. What entry displays a local policy from this display?

_____

```
HALIFAX                        27JUN MON  2245
                               29JUN WED  1700   RENTAL   1DAYS 18HRS
- - - - - - - - - - - - - - - - - - - - - - - - - - - - - - - - - - - - -
                    R C USD  RATE/PLAN MI/KM   CHG       APPROX C
  1 ZR DOLLAR    ECAR          16.34D   200    .07        37.59 O
  2 DS DISCOUNT  ECAN          18.79D   UNL    .00        43.23 I
  3 AC ACE RENT  ECAN          19.61D   200    .15        45.11 I
  4 ZD BUDGET    ECAN          19.61D   200    .15        45.11 I
```

The following question is based on the above Sabre shopper's car quote.

13. What entry displays a local policy for the least expensive in-terminal rental?

_____

14. Both corporate and local policy displays list 20 categories of information including address, telephone numbers and hours of operation. List at least five of the other categories that are displayed.

_____

_____

Supplementary Entries

Car Vendor Associates List

CARSFO

This entry will display a car vendor associates list, which is a list of car vendors who do business at the specified airport. The entry consists of the letters "CAR" followed by an airport code. This entry is useful if you have a client who wants to rent from a particular vendor and you need to find out if the vendor maintains a rental counter at the relevant airport.

Exercises

Don't forget to sign in to the emulator before beginning the exercises, and to sign out after finishing the last problem.

I. You have a client who will be staying in a hotel near London Heathrow airport. She would like to rent a car for a few days. Display a car vendor associates list for Heathrow. What entry did you make?

_____

In the United States, your client rents from Thrifty. Is there a Thrifty counter located at the Heathrow airport?

_____

II. Display a list of car vendors and their two-letter codes. What is the vendor code for Ace Rent a Car?

_____

III. Display a list of vehicle types and their meanings. How is a "CJMN" described?

_____

IV. Display the PNR for passenger Berenger. These clients would like to rent a car in Denver. They would like to request snow chains. Display a list of equipment codes to find the correct code for snow chains.

What entry did you make? _____

What is the correct code? _____

Ignore this PNR.

Format Review

Car Information Displays	`DU*/CAR/VENDOR`	Display a list of car vendors and their two-letter codes
	`DU*/CAR/TYPES`	Display a list of vehicle type codes and their meanings
	`DU*/CAR/EQP`	Display a list of equipment codes that may be used in the "SQ-" modifier
Car Rules	`CF*R1`	Display rules for the car on line 1 of a shopper's car quote display
	`CQ*R3`	Display rules for the car on line 3 of a single-company car quote display
Car Policy	`CP*ZECORP`	Display corporate policy for ZE
	`CP*ZELAX`	Display local policy for ZE at LAX
	`CQ*P`	Display local policy from a single-company car quote
	`CF*P4`	Display local policy from a shopper's car quote for the company on line 4
	`CP*`	Redisplay a policy display
Car Vendor Associates List	`CARYYZ`	Display a car vendor associates list for YYZ

LEARNING OUTCOMES

At the end of this lesson, you should be able to:

•Display an index of hotels
•Display a hotel description
•Display a rate description
•Book a hotel room

Hotel bookings are another source of commission for a travel agent. Many hotels rely on travel agents to recommend and sell their product. When you work in the industry, you'll learn about individual hotel properties through colleagues, seminars, promotional material and personal trips.

Using the Sabre SHAARP Plus system is a quick and easy way to secure a hotel booking for your client, especially when you've already booked air segments. There are four steps to booking a hotel room:

SHOP   Display a hotel index
LOOK   Display a hotel description
CHECK   Display a rate description
BOOK   Book the room

Review Questions

Hotel Index (SHOP)

```
1.2BENNETT/MALCOM MR/ANGIE MRS
 1 AC 138Y 25MAY 6 YVRYUL SS2      1415 2250 /DCAC /E
 2 AC 129Y 27MAY 1 YULYVR SS2      1915 2130 /DCAC /E
A0A0.A0A0*APL 1400/17FEB
```

The following question is based on the above partial Sabre PNR.

1.   What two entries will retrieve an index of hotels in Montreal (YUL) for the full duration of the Bennetts' stay?

_____

_____

```
QUALIFIERS - YUL/25MAY-2NT2/C-USD/RC-V,C,F,P,R,S,T,W
                                DIST N/C AMENITY    RATE RANGE
      1 BW ST JEROME            12SW    IP    D      65 -  81*
      2 HL AIRPORT               1SE    IPS   D     131 - 163*
      3 BW DORVAL                1E     IPS   D      57 -  74*
      4 QI LE BOULEVARD         14E     IP    D      52 -  63*
      5 QI AIRPORT               3NE    IP    D      61 -  70*
      6 HI AIRPORT               3NE    IPS   D      76 -  99*
      7 RA INN MONTREAL DOWNTWON 9E     IP    D      83 - 107*
      8 SI LE CENTRE             9E     IP    D     118 - 159*
      9 PH GRAND MONTREAL        9E     IP    D     131 - 209*
     10 LW RITZ CARLTON          9E     IP F  D     164 - 490*
     11 BW SHANGRILA             9E     I     D     108 - 108*
     12 RA OLYMPIC PARK          9E     IP    D      73 -  96*
     13 FS MONTREAL              9E     IP F  D     182 - 194*
     14 HI DOWNTOWN              9E     IP    D     101 - 145*
               -CUSTOM OFFERS -ACTUAL RATES  *-RATE ASSURED
    I-HSPD P-POOL S-FREE SHTL F-FITN B-FREE BKST D-DINE R-FREE PARK
```

The following six questions are based on the above Sabre hotel index.

2.   Which of these hotels offer a fitness center?

_____

3.   True or False: All these hotels offer dining options. Explain your answer.

_____

4.   How far and in what direction is the Holiday Inn (HI) Downtown from YUL (assume you are located in the U.S.)?

_____

5.   Which hotel offers the lowest room rate?

_____

6.   If your client wants to stay at the airport, which hotels would you recommend?

_____

7.   What is the entry to see more hotels in Montreal?

_____

```
QUALIFIERS - YUL/25MAY-2NT2/C-USD/RC-V,C,F,P,R,S,T,W
                                DIST N/C AMENITY    RATE RANGE
  15 RA RENAISSANCE DU PARC       9NE   IP    D     99 - 154*
  16 UI INTERCONTINENTAL         10E    IP    D     205 - 252*
                  -CUSTOM OFFERS -ACTUAL RATES *-RATE ASSURED
  I-HSPD P-POOL S-FREE SHTL F-FITN B-FREE BKST D-DINE R-FREE PARK
```

The following question is based on the above Sabre hotel index.

8. What entry returns this display to the screen beginning with line 1?

    _____

9. What entry redisplays the last hotel index?

    _____

Hotel Description (LOOK)

10. What entry displays a hotel description for the hotel on line 5 of an index display?

    _____

Hotel Rate Description (CHECK)

11. Rate descriptions contain specific information on the rates listed in the hotel description. What is the entry to display a rate description for the rate on line 3 of a description display?

    _____

Hotel Book (BOOK)

12. What is the entry to book one room at the rate listed on line 3 of a hotel rate display?

    _____

13. From what two displays is it possible to book a hotel room?

    _____

Booking A Hotel, A Complete Example

```
1.2HENDERSON/CHARLES MR/LAUREN MRS
 1 AC 795Y 19APR W YYZLAX SS2      325P    528P /DCAC /E
 2 AC 792Y 29APR J LAXYYZ SS2      130P    851P /DCAC /E
TKT/TIME LIMIT
   1.TAW12APR/
PHONES
   1.YYZ416 933 5844-A
   2.YYZ416 379 2665-H
A0A0.A0A0*AAB 1020/19MAR
```

The following question is based on the above partial Sabre PNR.

14. The Hendersons require a hotel for their full stay in Los Angeles (LAX). What entry displays the hotel index?

_____

```
QUALIFIERS - LAX/19APR-10NT2/C-USD/RC-V,C,F,P,R,S,T,W
                        DIST N/C AMENITY     RATE RANGE
    1 CY IRVINE/JOHN WAY     35SE      S       50 - 86*
    2 CO SAN PEDRO COMPR     17SE     IP F     88 - 130
    3 PW JOLLY ROGER INN     30E      IPS   D  65 - 100*
    4 TL ANAHEIM ALOHA       30E      IPS      42 - 49*
    5 VP ANAHEIM PLAZA       30E      IP       47 - 117
    6 BW APOLLO              29E      IPS   D  65 - 85*
    7 LZ DISNEYLAND          29E      IP    D 145 - 145*
    8 VP TROPICANA INN       30E      IP       68 - 140
    9 DI DAYSTOP ANAHEIM     25E      IPS      33 - 58*
   10 IT PALOS VERDES         9S      I S      90 - 110
   11 BW VALENICA INN        26E      IP       55 - 120*
   12 MC AIRPORT              1E        SF      1 - 17*
   13 DI FULLERTON-ANAHE      3E      IPSF     49 - 8*
   14 RD MANHATTAN BEACH      3SE      I S      79 - 16*
              -CUSTOM OFFERS -ACTUAL RATES *-RATE ASSURED
I-HSPD P-POOL S-FREE SHTL F-FITN B-FREE BKST D-DINE R-FREE PARK
```

The following question is based on the above Sabre hotel index.

15. The Hendersons belong to the Marriott Hotels Honored Guest Awards program and would like to stay at a Marriott (MC) hotel. What entry would you make to display the hotel description?

_____

```
HOD*12
                  ** DIRECT CONNECT AVAILABILITY **
                  ** MARRIOTT HOTELS RESPONSE **
MC7779 AIRPORT                          LAX
ADDR-     5855 W CENTURY BLVD              19APR - 1NT2
          LOS ANGELES CA 945              LOS ANGELES
PHONE-    213-641-57                    ** SELL H1LINENBR
                                        TAXES- 11 PCT


1 WEEKEND                               15.USD        /C- 6P
TTL TAX    115.5
APPROX. TOTAL PRICE    1165.5 USD
INCLUDES TAXES AND SURCHARGES


2 CORPORATE                             149.USD       /C- 6P
TTL TAX    163.9
APPROX. TOTAL PRICE    1653.9 USD
INCLUDES TAXES AND SURCHARGES


3 DELUXE 1 KING BED                     17.USD        /C- 6P
TTL TAX    187.
APPROX. TOTAL PRICE    1887. USD
INCLUDES TAXES AND SURCHARGES
```

The following two questions are based on the above Sabre hotel description.

16. What is the guarantee policy for these rooms?

_____

17. What entry displays a description of the rate for the deluxe room with 1 king bed?

_____

```
HRD*3
MC7779 AIRPORT                        LAX
ADDR-     5855 W CENTURY BLVD           19APR - 1NT2
          LOS ANGELES CA 945          LOS ANGELES
PHONE-    213-641-57                   ** SELL H13
                                    TAXES- 11 PCT
3    DELUXE 1 KING BED             17. USD  A1KRAC
APPROX. TOTAL PRICE   1887. USD
INCLUDES TAXES AND SURCHARGES
1887. TOTAL PRICE STARTING 19APR FOR 1 NIGHTS
    GUARANTEE   - 6 PM HOLD
    CANCELLATION- 6 PM
    COMMISSION - 1 PERCENT COMMISSION
    EXTRA PERSON- *    6. USD  ROLLAWAY  - *    8. USD
    TO SELL EXTRA PERSON USE          /EX-1
    TO SELL ROLLAWAY USE              /RA-1
    TO SELL CRIB USE                  /CR-1
```

The following two questions are based on the above Sabre hotel rate description.

18. What is the cancellation policy for this rate?

_____

19. What entry books the room detailed here?

_____

```
H1#3
DIRECT CONNECT RESPONSE RECEIVED
   HHL MC HK1 LAX IN19APR 6-OUT29APR  1NT  7779 AI    /DCMC
RPORT 1A1KRAC-2/17.USD/C6P/AGT987654321/SI-CF-FUX5CQ
```

The following four questions are based on the above Sabre hotel book response.

20. What is the hotels confirmation number for the reservation?

_____

21. For how many nights has the reservation been made?

_____

22. What is the product rate code and the hotel chain code?

_____

23. What does C06P indicate?

_____

```
1.2HENDERSON/CHARLES MR/LAUREN MRS
 1 AC 795Y 19APR W YYZLAX SS2     325P   528P /DCAC /E
 2  HHL MC HK1 LAX IN19APR 6-OUT29APR  1NT  7779 AI    /DCMC
RPORT 1A1KRAC-2/17.USD/C6P/AGT987654321/SI-CF-FUX5CQ
 3 AC 792Y 29APR J LAXYYZ SS2     13P    851P /DCAC /E
TKT/TIME LIMIT
   1.TAW12APR/
PHONES
  1.YYZ416 933 5844-A
  2.YYZ416 379 2665-H
AA.AA*AAB 127/19NOV
```

The following two questions are based on the above partial Sabre PNR.

24. What entries must be made to save the hotel booking in the PNR?

_____

25. If the Hendersons decide against this hotel booking, what entry, besides the entry to ignore, cancels the booking?

_____

Supplementary Entries

Hotel Index

In the online lesson, you display hotel indexes by referencing a flight segment. Hotel indexes may also be displayed directly, without an itinerary in the work area. Three such entries are shown below.

```
HOTLAX/12JAN-16JAN2
HOTLAX/12JAN-4NT2
```
These entries will display a hotel index in Los Angeles (LAX), for the dates January 12 to January 16, for two adults. These entries are used when you have a client who wants to book a hotel room, but does not require flights.

The first entry consists of the letters HOT, followed by a three-letter airport code, a slash, the check-in and check-out dates separated by a hyphen, and the number of adults who will be staying in the room. The second entry is exactly the same, except that the number of nights is specified, in the usual manner, instead of the check-out date.

HOTLAX

Sometimes when you display a hotel index with dates, the hotel you want to book will not be listed. This happens when the hotel has no rooms available for the dates specified. To see a list of hotels regardless of whether they are available, you may display an index without dates. The entry to do this is shown here. To book a room, however, you would need to give Sabre the stay dates and the number of adults.

Hotel Description

HOD*

This entry is used to redisplay a hotel description if it has been removed from your screen. It is simply the letters HOD followed by an asterisk.

Hotel Rate Description

HRD*

When a hotel rate description is removed from your screen, you may redisplay it using the entry shown here. This entry is the letters HRD followed by an asterisk.

Exercises

Dont forget to sign in to the emulator before beginning the exercises, and to sign out after finishing the last problem. When necessary, use the hotel encode and decode entries you learned in Lesson 2.

I.   Display the PNR for passenger Chamberlain and retrieve a hotel index for the full duration of the clients stay in New York.

What hotel chain operates the Island Inn? _____

How far is the Washington Square Hotel from New York, Kennedy airport?

_____

What mode of transportation is recommended to get to the Garden City hotel?

_____

Display a description for this hotel. What is the rate for a corporate room?

_____

Ignore the PNR.

II. Retrieve the PNR for Claudine and Louise Chantel, who require a hotel for their full stay in Chicago. They are interested in staying at the Sheraton (SI) Plaza Hotel. Make the entry to display an index for Chicago, and then display a description for this hotel.

What entry did you make to display the description?

_____

What is the least expensive rack rate available?

_____

What is the room type for this rate?

_____

Are pets allowed at this hotel?

_____

Is the pool at this hotel outdoor or indoor?

_____

How far away is this hotel from the University of Chicago?

_____

Ignore the PNR.

III.   Retrieve the PNR for Ms. Jeanine Ackers, who requires a hotel for her stay in Boston. Display a hotel index for Boston. (Hint: Remember that only one adult will be staying.) What entry did you use?

_____

Display a hotel description for the John Carver Inn.   On what street is it located?

_____

What are the two room types available at this hotel?

_____

What type of hotel is this?   What is its class rating?

_____

Ignore the PNR.

IV.   Retrieve the PNR for passenger Tessler and display a hotel index for the full stay in London. Display a hotel description for the first Sheraton hotel listed.

What are the taxes at this hotel?

_____

Are there tennis courts at this hotel?

_____

Book the lowest priced room with two beds. (Hint: This is the same entry you would use had you displayed a rate description.)

What entry did you make?

_____

Redisplay the itinerary. What is the hotel segment numbered?

_____

For how many nights has the hotel been booked?

_____

What is the confirmation number for the booking?

_____

Enter a received-from (Ms. Tessler) and end the transaction.

V. Retrieve the PNR for passenger Fromke and display an index in Minneapolis for the full stay. What amenities does the DX Minneapolis Bloomington offer?

_____

Display a description for this hotel and then book the superior room with 1 king bed.   What entry did you make?

_____

Enter a received-from (Mr. Fromke) and end the transaction.

VI. Mr. Simmons would like to book the least expensive single room in Boston, one month from today, for a 7-night stay.   Display a hotel index.

What hotel would you book for Mr. Simmons?

_____

VII. Display a basic hotel index with no dates to find the name of the FA hotel in Quebec City. What entry did you make?

_____

What chain is represented by the code FA?

_____

What is this hotels telephone number?

_____

Format Review

Hotel Index	HOT1/16JAN2	Display a hotel index for the arrival city and date of itinerary segment 1, with check-out on January 16, two adults
	HOT1/4NT2	As above, using the number of nights stay in place of a check-out date
	HOT*	Page down a hotel index
	HOT*1	Return to page 1 of a hotel index
	HOT**	Redisplay a hotel index
	HOTLAX/18JUN-25JUN2	Display a hotel index without referencing a flight segment
	HOTLAX/18JUN-7NT2	As above, using the number of nights stay
	HOTLAX	Display a hotel index, listing all hotels regardless of availability
Hotel Description	HOD*2	Display a hotel description for the hotel on line 2 of a hotel index
	HOD*	Redisplay a hotel description
Hotel Rate Description	HRD*2	Display a description for the rate on line 2
	HRD*	Redisplay a rate description
Hotel Book	H12	Book 1 room from line 2
Cancel Hotel Segment	X2	Cancel hotel segment number 2

LESSON **FOURTEEN**

LEARNING OUTCOMES

At the end of this lesson, you should be able to:

• **Add modifiers to a hotel index entry**
• **Add optional information to a hotel booking entry**

In this lesson, you learn how to add optional information to the hotel index and hotel booking entries. While optional in the format syntax, this extra information may be necessary to effectively search for or book the hotel room.

It's important to find the right hotel for your client, and, as always, your goal should be to accomplish this as quickly as possible. Using search qualifiers in the hotel index entry can really help, since qualifiers will significantly reduce the number of hotels in the display.

When a hotel requires a credit card guarantee to hold a reservation, you'll need to include this extra information in the hotel booking entry. Similarly, to provide the best possible service to your client, you may need to include special requests or membership numbers as well.

Review Questions

Hotel Index with Search Qualifiers

```
1.2LOBOS/MICHAEL MR/RACHEL MRS
 1 UA  685Y 18FEB F LGAORD SS2    130P   220P /DCUA /E
 2 UA  684Y 28FEB M ORDLGA SS2    100P   353P /DCUA /E
A0A0.A0A0*AAB 1801/26NOV
```

The following question is based on the above partial Sabre PNR.

1. Write down the entries to display the following hotel indexes for the Loboses' full stay in Chicago (ORD).

   All Hyatt (HY) hotels _____

   Cartwright Hotel _____

   Hotels with rooms priced at 200 or less of your currency _____

   Hotels with rooms priced at 100 or more of your currency _____

   Hotels with rooms priced between 100 and 200 _____

```
QUALIFIERS - LAX/C-USD/N-PARK/RC-V,C,F,P,R,S,T,W
                              DIST N/C AMENITY    RATE RANGE
   1 UI DAYS INN PARK           3E    I              69 - 79*
   2 UI PARK SUNSET            11N    IP        D    64 - 79*
                    -CUSTOM OFFERS -ACTUAL RATES *-RATE ASSURED
I-HSPD P-POOL S-FREE SHTL F-FITN B-FREE BKST D-DINE R-FREE PARK
```

The following question is based on the above Sabre hotel index.

2.   Why do these hotels both have "PARK" in their names?

_____

```
1.1KAWAMURA/SHIZUTO MR
 1 UA 837B 19MAR 7 SFONRT SS1   1340 1625   20MAR 1 /DCUA /E
 2 UA 828B 26MAR 7 NRTSFO SS1   1615 0930 /DCUA /E
A0A0.A0A0*AWA 1836/21FEB NKVVUZ
```

The following question is based on the above partial Sabre PNR.

3.   What entry will display a hotel index in Tokyo (NRT), for the passenger's full stay, listing prices in Japanese Yen (JPY)?

_____

4.   If you do not specify a currency in your hotel index entry, in what currency are prices listed?

_____

```
QUALIFIERS - SYD/C-USD/RC-V,C,F,P,R,S,T,W/HL,OM,HY
                              DIST N/C AMENITY    RATE RANGE
   1 OM RUSHCUTTER TVLO         6NE   IP        D   138 - 156*
   2 HY KINGSGATE               6NE   IP        D   130 - 256*
   3 HL SYDNEY                   5N    IP      F D   226 - 331*
   4 OM PARK ROYAL PARRAM        6N    IP        D   174 - 193*
   5 OM OLD SYDNEY PKRO          6N    IP        D   223 - 248*
   6 OM NORTH SYDNEY TL          7N    IP        D   178 - 206*
                    -CUSTOM OFFERS -ACTUAL RATES *-RATE ASSURED
I-HSPD P-POOL S-FREE SHTL F-FITN B-FREE BKST D-DINE R-FREE PARK
```

The following question is based on the above Sabre hotel index.

5. This display lists properties for three hotel chains. What search qualifier was used in the hotel index entry?

    _____

6. Can more than one search qualifier be used in a single hotel index entry?

    _____

**Optional
Booking Fields**

7. Write down the characters used in each of the optional booking fields.

    Request for an adult rollaway bed   _____

    Frequent traveler number   _____

    Special information field   _____

```
2  HHL RT HK1 SFO IN18JUN 6-OUT28JUN  10NT  22709 SO    /DCRT
   FITELSFO 1A1DRAC-2/150.00USD/EX20.00-2/RA20.00-2/C06P/AGT98765432
   1/SI-REQUEST ROOM BY ELEVATOR-CF-CZ9WD39I
```

The following four questions are based on the above Sabre hotel booking response.

8. What has been requested in the special information field?

    _____

9. How many extra adults in the room have been requested?

    _____

10. What is the cost for the extra adults?

    _____

11. Have rollaway beds been requested for the extra adults? What is the cost?

    _____

```
                ** DIRECT CONNECT AVAILABILITY **
                      ** DAYS INN RESPONSE **
        DI0061431 UNIVERSAL STUDI                  MCO
        ADDR-     5827 CARAVAN CT                  15MAY - 7NT2
                  ORLANDO FL 32819                 ORLANDO
        PHONE-    407-351-3800                     ** SELL 0H1LINENBR
                                            TAXES- 10 PCT


        1   CORPORATE                      69.00USD        /C- 4P
        TTL TAX     48.30
        APPROX. TOTAL PRICE    531.30 USD
        INCLUDES TAXES AND SURCHARGES


        2   GOVERNMENT                     62.00USD        /C- 4P
        TTL TAX     43.40
        APPROX. TOTAL PRICE    477.40 USD
        INCLUDES TAXES AND SURCHARGES


        3   MILITARY                       62.00USD        /C- 4P
        TTL TAX     43.40
        APPROX. TOTAL PRICE    477.40 USD
        INCLUDES TAXES AND SURCHARGES
```

The following question is based on the above Sabre hotel description.

12. Your clients, Dr. and Mrs. James Ing, qualify for the government rate. What entry books and guarantees this room with Mastercard (CA) 5193 1234 5555 6666, expiring in July of next year?

_____

Exercises   Don't forget to sign in to the emulator before beginning the exercises, and to sign out after finishing the last problem. Remember to use the hotel encode and decode entries from Lesson 2 when necessary.

1. Retrieve the PNR for passenger Mr. Adam Lim. Display a hotel index for the full stay in Paris, specifying all Utell and Best Western hotels. What entry did you make?

_____

Display a description for the first Best Western hotel listed. Then book a deluxe room with 1 double bed, guaranteeing it to Mr. Lim's Visa (VI) card (4378 002 188 936), which expires in February of next year.

What entry did you make?

_____

Enter a received-from (Mr. Lim) and end the transaction.

II.   Retrieve the PNR for passenger Candaux. These women were recommended a hotel in Tokyo, but cannot remember the full name. They know it contains the letters "OTAN". Make the entry to display a hotel index for hotels with these letters in their name, for the women's full stay in Tokyo.

What entry did you make?

_____

Display a description for the New Otani Hotel. Book the lowest priced room at the rack rate, specifying an extra adult and a rollaway bed.

What entry did you make?

_____

Is there a charge for the extra adult?

_____

Enter a received-from (Ms. Candaux) and end the transaction.

III. Retrieve the PNR for passenger Ashlin. The Ashlins are interested in a hotel in Beverly Hills. Display an index for their full stay in Los Angeles for two adults, requesting hotels with zip code "90210".

What entry did you make?

_____

How many hotels have been displayed?

_____

Display a description for the Beverly Hilton and book a standard room with 1 double bed, requesting a rollaway child's bed and a non-smoking room. What entry did you make?

_____

Enter a received-from (Mr. Ashlin) and end the transaction.

Format Review

Hotel Index with Search Qualifiers		
	HOT1/4NT2/HI	Display an index listing only those hotels in the HI chain, for a four-night stay beginning on the date in segment 1, for 2 adults
	HOT1/4NT2/HI,MC,HY	As previous, except for hotel chains HI, MC, and HY
	HOT3/6JUL2/N-PIER	Display hotel index listing only those hotels with the letters "PIER" in their name
	HOT1/15JUN2/C-EUR	Display hotel index listing prices in Euros (EUR)
	HOT1/15JUN2/PC-10301	Display hotel index for hotels with zip (postal) code 10301
	HOT2/3NT2/R-200	Display a hotel index listing only those hotels with rooms for 100 currency units a night or less (currency of country where SABRE set is located)
	HOT2/3NT2/R¥100	Display a hotel index listing only those hotels with rooms for 100 currency units a night or more (currency of country where SABRE set is located)
	HOT2/3NT2/R¥100/R-200	Display a hotel index listing only those hotels which sell for between 100 and 200 currency units
	HOT1/12AUG2/RC-W,C	Display a hotel index listing weekend (W) and corporate (C) rates

LESSON **FOURTEEN**

Optional Booking Fields

ØH1¥2/SI-RQST QUIET ROOM

Make a hotel booking, requesting a quiet room

ØH1¥2/RA-1

Make a hotel booking, requesting 1 adult rollaway bed

ØH1¥2/RC-1

Make a hotel booking, requesting 1 child's rollaway bed

ØH1¥2/CR-1

Make a hotel booking, requesting 1 crib

ØH1¥2/EX-1

Make a hotel booking, specifying 1 extra person

ØH1¥2/FT-AA9477KL

Make a hotel booking, specifying a frequent traveler ID number (airline code precedes number)

ØH1¥2/CD-38677K

Make a hotel booking, specifying a corporate ID number

ØH1¥2/ID-33KKK7

Make a hotel booking, specifying a hotel customer ID number

ØH1¥2/W

Make a hotel booking, requesting a written confirmation

ØH1¥2/GAX348822941152345EXP 1 16-SMITH

Make a hotel booking, guaranteeing the room to an American Express (AX) card

LESSON **FIFTEEN**

LEARNING OUTCOMES

At the end of this lesson, you should be able to:

• **Retrieve airfares (tariffs)**
• **Interpret fare displays**
• **Understand a fare inclusion code**
• **Understand how to retrieve child and infant fares**
• **Display fare rules**
• **Read fare rules**
• **Retrieve a fare display from availability**
• **Utilize fare display shortcut entries**

Airfares are complex. There are usually dozens or hundreds of fares for travel between any two cities. Each fare is uniquely identified by an alpha-numeric code called the fare basis. Normal fares are full adult fares for unrestricted (or less restricted) travel in first, business or coach class. These are the most expensive fares. Discounted fares are called "excursion fares". In general, the less expensive a fare, the more restrictions it carries. Most excursion fares are for the coach cabin of an aircraft, but you can sometimes find discounted fares in first and business class.

There are two ways to access fares in Sabre:

· Fare Displays (FQ)
· Itinerary Pricing (WP)

This lesson teaches the fare display (or tariff display). Fare displays are the fastest way to see a list of fares for travel between two cities, and to compare prices and restrictions. Prices do not include most taxes, and many of the fares may not be valid for your client's particular trip, so fares in tariff displays should never be used to quote trip prices to a client.

Normal and excursion fares are the most common fare types and Sabre will list both types in a fare display. If you want to see another type of fare, for example a government or military fare, you need to use a fare inclusion code in your entry. Similarly, special characters need to be added to the entry if you want to see child or infant fares. Since most airlines do not offer excursion child and infant fares, children are almost always booked at the regular adult fare, thus eliminating the need to display child and infant fares.

Every fare has a "rule display" which lists details about the fare, including a description of each restriction. Reading and understanding fare rules is an important skill for every travel agent. Travelers can book air travel on the Internet, but few can interpret and understand a fare's restrictions.

A few fare display shortcut entries are presented in the Supplementary Entries section of this chapter. You can practice these entries in the emulator if you wish to see how they work.

Review Questions

Fare Displays

1. Which of the following fare types has the most restrictions and is the least expensive: first class, business class, full coach/economy class or excursion?

    _____

2. The fare display action code "FQ" can be said to stand for "Fare Quote" but fare displays should not be used to quote the actual cost of a journey to a client. Why?

    _____

    _____

3. A Sabre fare display shows fares in the currency of . . .

    _____

4. What entry displays Air Canada's (AC) fares for travel from Toronto (YYZ) to Barbados (BGI) departing around April 18?

    _____

5. What entry displays fares for all airlines for travel from San Francisco (SFO) to Chicago (ORD) departing around November 10?

    _____

```
SFO-CHI        CXR-UA       SAT 30NOV                    USD
THE FOLLOWING CARRIERS ALSO PUBLISH FARES SFO-CHI:
AA CO DL US
   TAXES/FEES/U.S. PFC NOT INCLUDED-USE FT/FL/PXCHELP
   SEE N*/USTAX1 AND N*/USTAX2 FOR US DOMESTIC TAX INFORMATION
   ALL FEES/TAXES/SVC CHARGES INCLUDED WHEN ITINERARY PRICED
   SURCHARGE FOR PAPER TICKET MAY BE ADDED WHEN ITIN PRICED
   V FARE BASIS      BK     FARE   TRAVEL-TICKET AP  MINMAX  RTG
   1   QXE21NR       Q R   206.52  E27NV       21/1 SU/  -    2
   2   QWE21NR       Q R   226.98  E27NV       21/1 SU/  -    2
   3   HXE14NR       H R   247.46  E27NV       14/1 SU/  -    2
   4   HWE14NR       H R   266.06  E27NV       14/1 SU/  -    2
   5   HXE7P50       H R   293.96  E28NV        7/1 SU/  -    2
   6   HWE7P50       H R   310.70  E28NV        7/1 SU/  -    2
   7   VA0AN         V R   340.96  E28NV         /1 SU/ 30    2
   8   BA7           B X   493.70  E28NV        7/  -/   -    2
   9   BA134         B X   563.73  E28NV        ¥¥  -/   -    2  ¥
```

The following seven questions are based on the above Sabre fare display.

6.   When does the fare on line 3 become effective?

_____

7.   What is the fare basis code for the least expensive round-trip fare shown in this screen of fares?

_____

8.   What is the fare basis code for the least expensive one-way fare shown in this screen of fares?

_____

9.   Explain the advance purchase requirements for the fares on lines 6, 7 and 8:

     "7/1" _____

     _____

     "/1" _____

     "7/" _____

10. What does the "¥" symbol mean in the advance purchase column for the fare on line 9?

_____

11. What is the minimum stay requirement for the fares on lines 1 through 7?

_____

12. Do the prices listed here include the applicable taxes?

_____

```
YTO-SYD        SHOP         SUN 10JUN                           CAD
AC  0/ 1/ 3   NZ  0/ 0/ 0   QF  0/ 1/ 0
   SURCHARGE FOR PAPER TICKET MAY BE ADDED WHEN ITIN PRICED
   INTL TAXES/FEES/US PFC - NOT INCL IN TOTAL
**      YTOSYD.EH        10JUN
   V FARE BASIS      BK     FARE   CX   TRAVEL-TICKET AP      MINMAX
 1   HXABD1M         H R   916.00  NZ   ES19MY D10JN  7/      5/30
 2   HWABD1M         H R   980.00  NZ   ES19MY D10JN  7/      5/30
 3   KLAP            K R  1300.00  AC   E19MY        21/      7/60
 4   BLAP1           B R  1378.00  NZ     —          14/      5/90
 5   BLAP            B R  1384.00  AC   E19MY        14/      5/180
 6   MKWAB1          H R  1404.00  NZ     —          21/      7/60
 7   MKXAB1          H R  1404.00  NZ     —          21/      7/60
 8   KKAP            K R  1552.00  AC   E19MY        21/      7/60
 9   YLEE            Y R  1632.00  NZ     —           -       5/-  ¥
```

The following four questions are based on the above Sabre fare display.

13. Fares for three airlines are included in this fare quote, though you can only see fares for two airlines in this portion of the display. What entry retrieved this fare display?

_____

14. What carrier offers the KKAP fare?

_____

15. What airlines offer direct flights between Toronto (YTO) and Sydney (SYD)?

_____

16. Recall that international fare displays organize fares into sections by global indicator. What is the two-letter global indicator code for the fares shown in this display and what does a global indicator signify?

_____

_____

17. What characters are added to a fare entry to display child fares and where in the entry are they placed?

_____

Rule Displays

18. What entry displays rules for the fare on line 3 of a fare display?

_____

```
V FARE BASIS      BK     FARE    TRAVEL-TICKET AP   MINMAX   RTG
1 LAB30           L R    3768      —        7/3 SU/30   EH01
FROM-OSL TO-LON CARRIER-BA  TRAVEL-18JUL    RULE 4410-IPREUP
FARE BASIS-LAB30     RT-SUPER SPECIAL APEX              SPECIAL FARE

NONREF/CHANGE SUBJECT TO FEE

01 BK CODE     - L -
02 PENALTY     - TKT IS NONREFUNDABLE BEFORE AND AFTER
         DEPARTURE IN CASE OF CANCELLATION/ REFUND - WAIVER
         APPLIES IN CASE OF A TICKET UPGRADE/ DEATH OF THE    ¥
```

The following three questions are based on the above Sabre rule display.

19. What booking code must be used for this fare?

_____

20. What is the penalty to cancel a booking after the ticket has been issued?

_____

21. What is the fare basis code for this fare?

_____

Supplementary Entries

Fare Displays from Availability

Sometimes when you are looking up fares for a client, you may need to display flight availability first, to determine what airline operates the most desirable flight (i.e., a non-stop flight or a flight departing closest to the time your client wishes to travel). Sabre has shortcut entries to help you move quickly from the CPA display to the fare display.

```
FQL1
FQL1/2
```

These entries are used to retrieve fares from CPA. They will retrieve a single-airline fare display for the airline, city pair, and date of a flight in a CPA display. The entry is the "FQ" action code followed by the letter "L" for "line" and a CPA line number. Two line numbers, separated with a slash, are specified for a connection.

Shortcut Entries

Sabre has many shortcut entries that are used to redisplay and/or change an existing fare display. The most commonly used entries are shown here.

```
FQ*
```

This entry is used to redisplay a fare quote when it is removed from your screen; for example, when a PNR is displayed. This redisplay entry is simply the "FQ" action code followed by an asterisk.

```
FQ*-AC
FQ*-AC-DL
```

These entries change the airline in a fare quote. For example, if your original FQ entry specified fares for AA, the FQ*-AC entry changes the fare display to show fares for AC instead. These entries are the "FQ" action code followed by an asterisk and the airline(s) for which you wish to see fares. Each airline code is always preceded by a hyphen.

```
FQ*21MAR
```

This entry changes the date in a fare quote. The entry is the "FQ" action code followed by an asterisk and the new date.

Exercises

Don't forget to sign in to the emulator before beginning the exercises, and to sign out after finishing the last problem.

I.   You have a client who is interested in going to Pittsburgh for his 25-year class reunion. Display fares for US Airways from San Francisco to Pittsburgh for travel two weeks from Thursday.

What is the fare basis code for the least expensive fare?

_____

Would this fare work if your client departed San Francisco on Thursday and returned that Saturday afternoon? Explain your answer.

_____

What fare would you recommend for your client for these travel dates?

_____

What would be the cost of this fare for a round trip to Pittsburgh?

_____

If your client departs two weeks from Thursday, on what date must the ticket be purchased for this fare?

_____

II. Display availability for travel from San Francisco to Los Angeles one week from today, departing around 9:00 a.m. (If today is Saturday or Sunday, use a week from Monday instead.) Display fares for United Airlines from this display.

Besides the price, what's the difference between the two least expensive fares (on lines 1 and 2)?

_____

These two fares are booked in "Q". Does the United flight departing around 9:00 a.m. have a "Q" booking code? Redisplay the current availability display to find out.

_____

III. Make the entry to display fares from Sydney, Australia to Frankfurt, Germany on Qantas. Specify a travel date of December 8. Move down the display as necessary to answer the following questions.

What is the two-letter global indicator for the fares in the first section of the display?

_____

What is the global indicator for the second section of fares?

_____

What is the global indicator for the third section of fares?

_____

The meaning of each global indicator is shown at the end of the fare display. What are the meanings of the three global indicators used in this fare display?

_____

_____

IV. What is the cost of the least expensive round-trip fare from New York, Kennedy to Calgary for travel departing one week from today?

_____

What airline offers this fare?

_____

What is the fare basis code of this fare?

_____

V. If today's date is between January 1 and June 30: Retrieve a single-airline display of Air France's (AF) fares for travel from Toronto to Paris, de Gaulle on November 12.

If today's date is between July 1 and December 31: Retrieve a single-airline display of Air France's (AF) fares for travel from Toronto to Paris, de Gaulle on February 12.

Your client needs to stay in Paris for 45 days. What is the price and fare basis code of the least expensive fare suitable for your client?

_____

In what booking code would you sell this fare?

_____

VI. Retrieve a shopper's display of fares for travel from Chicago to Paris, France for two weeks from today.

What entry did you make? _____

Who publishes the least expensive business-class fare (C or J)?

_____

Make the entry to redisplay the fares to show fares for United Airlines and American Airlines only.

What entry did you make? _____

Are United Airlines' and American Airlines' business class fares the same price?

_____

Display the PNR for passenger Difford. Then redisplay the fare display.

What entry did you make? _____

Make the entry to clear the work area.

VII. Display availability from San Francisco to Miami for the second Saturday from today at 9:00 p.m. Then make the shortcut entry to display fares for the first airline listed.

What entry did you make? _____

What is the fare basis and price of the least expensive fare?

_____

What is the advance purchase requirement of this fare?

_____

Make the entry to redisplay availability and then scroll down to the connection leaving at 11:30 p.m. Make the shortcut entry to display fares for this airline.

What entry did you make? _____

Take note of the details of the least expensive fare listed and change the date of the display to ten days later.

What entry did you make? _____

If your client travels to Miami on this date instead, is the least expensive fare less, more or the same as the last fare you looked at?

_____

Besides the fare basis code and price, how else does this fare differ from the last fare you looked at?

_____

Format Review

Fare Displays	FQEZECDG23OCT-AF	Display adult normal and excursion fares (NLX, the default fare type) for AF from EZE to CDG on October 23
	FQEZECDG23OCT-AF-RG	As previous, but for AF and RG only
	FQYVRYYZ10NOV	Display fares from YVR to YYZ for November 10 for all airlines
	FQJFKLHR9APR,C	Display child fares for all airlines
	FQJFKLHR9APR,I	Display infant fares for all airlines
	FQJFKLHR9APREX-BA	Display "EX" (excursion) fares
Rules Display	RD4	Display rules for the fare on line 4 of a fare display
Scrolling	MT	Move to the top of a Sabre display
Fare Displays from CPA	FQL1	Retrieve fares for the flight on line 1 of a CPA display
	FQL1/2	Retrieve fares for the connecting flights on lines 1 and 2 of a CPA display
Shortcut Entries	FQ*	Redisplay "FQ" fare display
	FQ*-AC	Redisplay the "FQ" fare display to show fares for Air Canada (AC)
	FQ*21MAR	Redisplay the "FQ" fare display to show fares for 21 March

LEARNING OUTCOMES

At the end of this lesson, you should be able to:

• Price an itinerary
• Find the lowest price for an itinerary
• Store a fare in a pricing record
• Use secondary action codes in a pricing entry
• Price a child passenger
• Understand when to use FP lines

Itinerary pricing is the best way to determine the actual cost of a client's trip. Sabre will find the price of a booked air itinerary, taking into consideration fare rules and restrictions, and include all applicable ticket taxes. It can also search for a lower fare for the itinerary. The Sabre itinerary pricing function should be used on all of the PNRs you book.

The basic itinerary pricing entry "WP" can be expanded with secondary action codes to modify the price or store information required for ticketing. In Canada, agents use secondary action codes to store the itinerary and purpose of travel codes that the BSP requires on each ticket. You can also use secondary action codes to request child fares, as you will learn in the Supplementary Entries section of this chapter.

Review Questions

Itinerary Pricing

1. What is the primary action code for the itinerary pricing entries?

    _____

2. What does the entry WP do?

    _____

```
1.1ALLAN/MICHAEL MR
 1 QF 510F 08FEB T SYDBNE HK1    850A 1010A /DCQF*94U7PA /E
 2 QF 511F 11FEB F BNESYD HK1    845A 1010A /DCQF*94U7PA /E
TKT/TIME LIMIT
  1.TAW15JAN/
PHONES
  1.SYD02 992 1234-A
  2.SYD02 356 7652-H
  3.SYD02 676 8921-B
RECEIVED FROM - P
A0A0.A0A0*AMB 2358/05JAN GGXQQF
```

The following three questions are based on the above Sabre PNR.

3. What entry will display the fare for this itinerary, as it is currently booked?

    _____

4. What entry will display the lowest available fare for this itinerary, in any booking code?

    _____

5. What entry will display the lowest available fare for this itinerary, rebooking it in the corresponding booking code?

    _____

```
02DEC DEPARTURE DATE- - -LAST DAY TO PURCHASE 04NOV
            BASE FARE                    TAXES              TOTAL
   2-    CAD230.00                     61.48XT        CAD291.48ADT
      XT     16.10XG      33.15US     8.15XY     4.08XF
            460.00                      122.96            582.96TTL
ADT-02 VLWFLYAC VLXFLYAC
YVR AC LAX Q7.50 113.00VLWFLYAC AC YVR Q.750 102.00VLXFLYAC
215.00END XFLAX3
  1 AC 501V 02DEC 6 YVRLAX SS2   0730 1020 /DCAC
  2 AC 504V 07DEC 4 LAXYVR SS2   1115 1358 /DCAC
```

The following six questions are based on the above Sabre pricing response.

6. This Bargain Finder itinerary pricing response is for a PNR with two passengers. What is the per person base fare in CAD?

    _____

7. What is the total tax per person?

    _____

8. What is the total fare for both passengers?

    _____

9. The airline ticket must be issued by . . .

    _____

10. What ticketing arrangement entry would you make for the PNR?

    _____

11. The journey was rebooked in "V" booking code, but the fare basis code differs slightly for each segment. What is the fare basis code for each of the two segments?

_____

```
14DEC DEPARTURE DATE- - -LAST DAY TO PURCHASE 07DEC
          BASE FARE                  TAXES              TOTAL
1-    USD190.00                    35.40XT         USD225.40ADT
   XT    24.40US      6.00XY        2.00XA            3.00XF
         190.00                     35.40             225.40TTL
ADT-01 QXRM
 LAX DL MEX95.00QXRM DL LAX95.00QXRM NUC190.00END ROE1.
 000000 XFLAX3
CHANGE BOOKING CLASS -    1Q 2Q
```

The following four questions are based on the above Sabre pricing response.

12. This is a WPNC response, which means the itinerary was not rebooked in the lowest booking code. The display is exactly the same as the WP display, except that it contains a message telling you the code for which each segment must be rebooked. This is a two-segment PNR. In what code must each segment be rebooked?

_____

13. The linear fare calculation is shown on the two lines above the information to rebook. Read the linear fare calculation, and answer the following questions:

This is a round trip from Los Angeles (LAX) to what city? _____

What airline flies the first segment? _____

What airline flies the second segment? _____

The price is the same for each segment. What is this price? _____

The fare basis code is the same for each segment. What is it? _____

14. The NUC fare was converted to the currency of trip origin, United States dollars (USD). What is the total fare, including taxes, for the trip?

_____

15. What is the last date that the ticket may be purchased?

_____

PQ Records and FP Lines

16. Suppose you have just made an itinerary pricing entry. What is the entry that will store the current pricing information in a price quote record?

_____

17. It is also possible to create a price quote record at the same time the itinerary is priced. Write down a WP entry that will create a price record.

_____

18. If you create a price quote record before creating a name field, what must you do before ending the PNR to ensure that the PQ record is saved? Write down the entry to do this, assuming the PQ record (record 1) is for all passengers.

_____

_____

```
1.2CHAMBERLAIN/LARRY MR/CATHERINE MRS
 1 AA 918B 24FEB 3 MIAJFK HK2  0715 1002 /DCAA*NUW5JK /E
 2 AA1819B 05MAR 5 JFKMIA HK2  1230 1529 /DCAA*NUW5JK /E
TKT/TIME LIMIT
  1.TAW30JAN/
PHONES
  1.MIA305-376-2757-A
  2.MIA305-726-9120-B CATHERINE
PRICE QUOTE RECORD EXISTS
RECEIVED FROM - CATHERINE CHAMBERLAIN
A0A0.A0A0*ANB 0912/28JAN NUW5JK
```

The following two questions are based on the above Sabre PNR.

19. Mr. Chamberlain will pay for his ticket with a check, while Mrs. Chamberlain will use her company credit card. What entries add the Future Pricing lines referencing the first price quote record? Catherine's credit card is VI 4511 6789 7890 1234, expiring in July of 2013.

_____

_____

20. What entry will display the PQ record in this PNR?

_____

21. What entry displays a PQ summary, which shows each passenger name number and the PQ record linked with that name?

_____

```
                  PRICE QUOTE RECORD - DETAILS

FARE NOT GUARANTEED UNTIL TICKETED

PQ 1  HØ¥J2
         BASE FARE                    TAXES           TOTAL
         CAD425.6Ø                    99.19XT         CAD524.79ADT
     XT       34.28US      24.49XG     15.ØØSQ        11.22CA
              7.95XY        3.41XF      2.84AY
ADT-Ø1  Y1
 YMQ AC NYC Q7.5Ø Q14.3Ø 191.ØØY1 AC YMQ Q7.5Ø Q14.3Ø 1
 91.ØØY1 NUC374.9ØEND ROE1.135240 XFLGA3
Ø1   YUL AC   746Y  21MAY  1Ø5P Y1
Ø2 Ø LGA AC   747Y  Ø2JUN  1Ø5P Y1
     YUL
VALIDATING CARRIER-AC
AØAØ AØAØ *AAB 17Ø1/Ø7MAY                             PRICE-SYS
```

The following two questions are based on the above Sabre price quote record.

22. What secondary action codes were used to price the itinerary?

_____

23. What is the number of this price quote record?

_____

24. Does storing the fare in a PQ record guarantee the price of the ticket when it is finally issued?

_____

Supplementary Entries

Pricing a Child Passenger

When you make the "WP" entry, Sabre prices all passengers at an adult fare. If a child is traveling, you can ask Sabre to search for a child's fare in the chance that the airline may publish one for the market. When booking first, business or full coach class you should always check for a child's fare, since most children's fares are published in these normal fare categories.

Children are passengers aged 2 through 11.

```
WPRQ¥PADT/C06
```
This is an entry to price an itinerary and create a PQ record, pricing the first passenger as an adult (ADT) and the second passenger as a child, aged 6 (C06).

The passenger type secondary action code is separated from the rest of the entry with a "¥" character. It consists of the letter "P" for "passenger" followed by two passenger type codes, separated with a "/". The code "ADT" stands for adult and the code "C06" stands for a child, age 6. The entry shown above tells Sabre that the first passenger is an adult and the second passenger is a child of 6 years.

If there is more than one adult, you may specify a number before the passenger type code, like this:

```
WPRQ¥P2ADT/C11/C03
```
This entry tells Sabre that the first two passengers are adults, the third passenger is a child aged 11, and the fourth, a child aged 3. The passenger type codes must be kept in the same order as in the PNR name field.

Exercises

Don't forget to sign in to the emulator before beginning the exercises, and to sign out after finishing the last problem.

I.   Retrieve the PNR for passenger Margulies.

   What is the total per-passenger price for this trip, as it is currently booked?

   _____

   Does this trip qualify for a lower fare? If so, what is the booking code and total per-passenger price for the lower fare?

   _____

   By what day must the ticket be issued? If necessary, change the ticketing arrangement field to reflect this date.

   _____

   Rebook the itinerary at the lowest available fare and store the pricing information in a price quote record. If you are in Canada, include the itinerary code 0 and the travel code 2.

   Enter a received-from (Mr. Margulies) and end the PNR.

II.   Retrieve the PNR for passenger Lerat. Air Canada (AC) has just introduced a new, lower fare for travel from Toronto to Japan. Make the entry to determine if the passengers are eligible for this fare, rebooking them in the appropriate booking code if they are.

   What is the cost per passenger, including taxes? Record the cost in the currency of your own country.

   _____

   What is the last day to purchase the ticket?

   _____

Does the ticketing arrangement field need to be changed? If so, make the entry to change it, recording your entry here.

_____

Make the entry to store the pricing information in a price quote record. If you are located in Canada, make the entry which will include the itinerary code 7 and the travel code 2.

_____

Add a received-from (Emma) and end the PNR.

III. Retrieve the PNR for passenger Allan and price the itinerary as booked.

Note that this display has given you the price of the trip both in Australian dollars and your own currency. What is the base cost of the trip in Australian dollars?

_____

What is the total cost of the trip in your own currency?

_____

Ignore this PNR.

IV. Build and price a PNR for the following booking scenario. Before you end transaction, answer the questions that follow. If you are located in the United States, book flights from New York, Kennedy and use the area code 212. If you are located in Canada, book flights from Toronto, Pearson and use the area code 416.

Marcia Powell, a graduate student in psychology, has been invited to present a paper at a seminar in Holland. She needs to fly to Amsterdam, the capital of the Netherlands, three weeks from Wednesday, returning one week later. She has no preference for her departure times. Book Marcia a seat in the least expensive booking code on KLM's direct flights.

Your agency telephone number is 293-2100. Ms. Powell's home number is 209-8099. The tickets should be issued on the last possible day, and will be paid for with MasterCard (CA) number 5011 8009 2876 8000, expiring in December of next year. Ms. Powell came in to make the reservation herself, which is considered a business trip. Store the pricing information in a price quote record.

What is the base fare for this trip? _____

What is the total fare? _____

In what booking code are the flights booked? _____

What date did you enter in the ticketing field? _____

End the transaction.

V. Display the PNR for passenger Atwood. Price the itinerary, specifying the correct passenger types for the adults and children, and store the information in a price quote record.

What entry did you make? _____

What is the cost for each adult? _____

What is the cost for each child? _____

Now delete the PQ records. What entry did you make?_____

Ignore the PNR.

Format Review

Itinerary Pricing	`WP`	Display the price for a PNR as booked
	`WPH9¥J1`	Price the itinerary, specifying Canadian secondary action codes: itinerary code "9" and travel code "1".
Bargain Finder Fare Search	`WPNC`	Display the lowest available fare for an itinerary
	`WPNCB`	Display and rebook in the lowest available fare
Price Quote Records	`PQ`	Store the information from the currently active pricing display in a price quote (PQ) record in the PNR
	`WPRQ`	Price an itinerary and create a price quote record in one step
	`WPRQ¥PADT/CØ6`	Price a PNR with a child passenger and create a price quote record
	`*PQ`	Display details for all PQ records in the PNR
	`*PQS`	Display a summary of all PQ records in the PNR
	`*PQN1.3`	Display the PQ record linked to name 1.3
Link/Unlink PQ Records	`PQL1*ALL`	Link PQ record 1 to all names in the PNR
	`PQL2*N1.3`	Link PQ record 2 to name 1.3
	`PQL1*N1.1/1.2`	Link PQ record 1 to names 1.1 and 1.2
	`PQU1*ALL`	Unlink PQ record 1 from all names in the PNR
	`PQU2*N1.3`	Unlink PQ record 2 from name 1.3
	`PQU1*N1.1-1.3`	Unlink PQ record 1 from names 1.1 through 1.3

Deleting PQ Records

PQD-ALL   Delete all PQ records

PQD3   Delete PQ record 3

FP Lines

FPPQ1¥N1.1¥F*AX372842345671000/1016

Create an FP line referencing PQ record 1, passenger 1.1, specifying the form of payment as an American Express (AX) credit card expiring in October 2016

FP¤   Delete an FP line in a PNR

FP2¤   Delete FP line 2 in a PNR

Redisplay

*P   Display the passenger data field

Canadian Routing Codes

First Digit - Itinerary Code

0   United States (wholly within the USA) or transborder Canada-USA or USA-Canada
1   Mexico, Central America, Canal Zone, Costa Rica
2   Caribbean Islands & Countries of Caribbean, Bermuda including Puerto Rico and the US Virgin Islands
3   South America
4   Europe, including Morocco, Tunisia, Algeria, Greenland
5   Africa
6   Middle East and Western Asia
7   Asia, including India
8   Australia, New Zealand and the Islands of the Pacific including Hawaii, excluding Guam
9   Canada (wholly within Canada) or between Canada and St. Pierre et Miquelon

Second Digit - Purpose of Travel Code

1   Business
2   Travel
3   Selected Charters
9   Travel Agent Service Fee

LESSON **SEVENTEEN**

LEARNING OUTCOMES

At the end of this lesson, you should be able to:

•Issue a ticket for a PNR
•Display an ETR
•Read an ETR
•Void an ETR

The purpose of building a PNR is, of course, to issue a ticket for air travel. Air tickets are electronic records stored in the GDS. A traveler presents ID when checking in at the airport, and his or her electronic ticket record (ETR) is accessed via the computer system.

The entry to issue an airline ticket in Sabre is simple. The difficult part of ticketing is correctly building the PNR, finding the best fare, and then storing the fare in the PNR; all of which you've spent most of this course learning to do.

Being able to read an electronic ticket record (ETR) is an important skill. Be sure to spend adequate time in the lesson or emulator learning this skill.

Remember that you may build your own PNRs in the emulator and issue tickets. If your instructor has activated the "PNR Save Enabled" feature, the PNR and ETR will be saved in the VIASINC database and you may retrieve and manipulate them as on the live system.

Review Questions

Ticketing

1. What is the entry to issue airline tickets, referencing price quote record 1?

_____

```
1.1ANDOVER/MARK MR
 1 AC 764Y 11FEB F LAXYYC HK1   1210P   357P /DCAC*4182UU /E
 2 AC 763Y 19FEB J YYCLAX HK1    920A  1120A /DCAC*4182UU /E
TKT/TIME LIMIT
  1.T-11JAN-A0A0*AAB
PHONES
  1.LAX213-776-9164-A
  2.LAX213-982-4009-B
PRICE QUOTE RECORD EXISTS
REMARKS
  1.XXTAW11JAN/
RECEIVED FROM - PASSENGER
A0A0.A0A0*AUM 1045/12JAN GWAIOR
```

The following two questions are based on the above Sabre PNR.

2. What two lines in this PNR indicate that it has been ticketed?

_____

3.   On what date was the PNR ticketed?

_____

```
ELECTRONIC TICKET RECORD
INV:437198          CUST:                          PNR:YYZUGL
TKT:0161082738292   ISSUED:11JAN   PCC:A0A0   IATA:987654321
NAME:PHAM/NUYGEN MR                 FF: 27382672009
NAME REF:
FOP:*CA5276522091927901¥10/14
CPN A/L  FLT  CLS DATE   BRDOFF  TIME  ST F/B      STAT
  1  UA  2003   F  08FEB  SFOLAX  620A  OK F9       OPEN
  2  UA  2956   F  08FEB  LAXSFO  505P  OK F9       OPEN

FARE USD472.56 TAX  35.44 US TAX   7.50 XF TAX  11.00 XT
TOTAL USD526.50

SFO UA LAX 236.28F9 UA SFO 236.28F9 USD 472.56 END
XT 6.00ZP 5.00AY ZPSFOLAX XFSFO4.5LAX3
```

The following question is based on the above Sabre ETR.

4.   Read the above Electronic Ticket Record (ETR) and answer the following
      questions:

      When was this ticket issued? _____

      At what fare basis was the ticket issued? _____

      What is the total price of the ticket, including taxes? _____

      What is the 13-digit e-ticket number? _____

      "016" in the ticket number is . . . _____

      What is the passenger's frequent flyer number? _____

      What is the status of the flight coupons? _____

5.   True or False: An ETR is always for a single passenger, regardless of the
      number of passengers in the PNR.

_____

```
TKT/TIME LIMIT
  1.T-120CT-AØAØ*ANS
  2.TE 0011086273822-AT SINGH/L AØAØ*ANS 1255/120CT
  3.TE 0011086273823-AT SINGH/R AØAØ*ANS 1255/120CT
  4.TE 0011086273824-AT LEE/CON AØAØ*ANS 1255/120CT
```

The following question is based on the above Sabre TKT/TIME LIMIT field.

6.   What entry will display the e-ticket record (ETR) for R. Singh from the above list?

_____

Exercises

1.   Display the PNR for Tammy Weller.

Has a ticket been issued for the PNR?

_____

When was the ticket issued: today or yesterday?

_____

Every electronic ticket is identified by a unique 13-digit number. What entry could you make to see the ticket number?

_____

Display Tammy's e-ticket record (ETR). What two entries did you make?

_____

How did the customer pay for her ticket?

_____

Tammy wants to verify that British Airways has her frequent flyer number. Is there a frequent flyer number recorded on the e-ticket?

_____

What is the 13-digit e-ticket number?

_____

Where is the e-ticket number located in the ticketing field?

_____

Ignore the PNR.

Format Review

Ticketing

WETP*DL	Check Delta's (DL) policy on e-ticketing
W¥	Issue tickets for a PNR with FP lines. Either electronic or paper tickets will be issued, depending on default.
EW¥	End PNR and issue tickets for a PNR which contains FP lines
W¥PQ1	Issue tickets for a PNR, reading ticketing information from PQ record 1
EW¥PQ1	End PNR and issue tickets, reading ticketing information from PQ record 1
W¥PQ1¥XETR	Issue paper tickets, overriding e-ticket default
*T	Display the ticket/time limit field
WETR*2	Display the ETR (Electronic Ticket Record) for line 2 in ticket/time limit field
WETR*T0028273383834	Display the ETR for ticket number 0028273383834
WV3	Void the currently displayed electronic ticket, where 3 is the line number from the ticket/time limit field

LESSON **EIGHTEEN**

LEARNING OUTCOMES

At the end of this lesson, you should be able to:

•**Explain a PNR queue**
•**Display a count of PNRs on a queue**
•**Access a PNR queue**
•**Place a PNR on a queue**

To "queue" is to form a line while waiting. In computer terms, a queue is a sequence of stored data awaiting processing. A GDS uses queues for organizing PNRs that require action. Queues are also used to facilitate communication between airlines, travel suppliers and travel agencies. Remember that the airline has a copy of the traveler's PNR in its computer system. If a flight is canceled or undergoes a time change, the airline will modify the PNR and send it to one of your agency's queues. Likewise, if a special service request cannot be confirmed, an airline will modify the status code in the SSR message and place the PNR on a queue. Other travel suppliers can communicate with your office in the same manner, by placing a message in the PNR and putting it on a queue in your office.

In the online lesson, you have a chance to practice using PNR queues. You learn how to count the number of PNRs on a queue, how to access and work through a queue, and how to place a PNR on a queue.

Review Questions

Queues and Queue Count

1. What is a queue in a GDS (Global Distribution System)?

    _____

    _____

2. List three reasons why an airline might queue a PNR for your attention.

    _____

    _____

    _____

3. What entry lists the number of PNRs on each agency queue, excluding those which are empty?

    _____

```
ON QUEUE AS OF   5Ø7P ON 29NOV FOR AØAØ
    1.....4      6.....8     18.....3     7Ø.....2
    5.....7      9.....1     4Ø.....4     83.....5

TOTAL  MESSAGES.......Ø  SPECIAL........Ø  PNRS..........47
```

The following two questions are based on the above Sabre queue count.

4. How many PNRs have been placed on Queue 18, the Waitlist Confirmation Queue?

   _____

5. How many PNRs have been placed on Queue 25? Explain your answer.

   _____

6. What entry shows how many PNRs are waiting for action specifically on Queue 9, the Ticketing Queue?

   _____

Queue Access

7. Ending a PNR while on queue will . . .

   _____

8. Ignoring a PNR while on queue will . . .

   _____

9. What entry signs on to the Waitlist Confirmation Queue (18)?

   _____

10. Suppose that as soon as you start checking the queues, the office telephones start ringing and you notice a client waiting to be served. What single entry signs you off the current queue and ignores the last transaction?

   _____

11. You have just notified some clients that their flights have cleared the waitlist and are now confirmed. You have also updated the PNR as required. How do you simultaneously end the PNR and exit the queue?

_____

Queue Placement

12. Recall that each travel consultant who works in a travel agency can be assigned a personal queue. Suppose that you have just booked flights for a client who also requires a hotel. If your queue number is 65, what entry adds a queue placement remark to remind you to book a hotel on June 18? The prefatory code for "need hotel" is 60.

_____

13. You have just built a PNR for one of your colleague's clients but do not have time to add some of the optional fields required to complete the booking. If your colleague's queue number is 35, what entry places the PNR on her queue, with a reminder to book a special meal? The prefatory code for "special meal" is 18.

_____

Exercises

Don't forget to sign in to the emulator before beginning the exercises, and to sign out after finishing the last problem.

I. Make the entry to determine how many PNRs have been placed on Queue 5, a schedule change queue.

How many PNRs have been placed on this queue? _____

II. Make the entry to display a queue count for all agency queues.

How many PNRs are on Queue 6? _____

How many PNRs are on Queue 40? _____

III. Make the entry to sign on to Queue 6 and then answer the following questions.

What is the prefatory instruction for this queue? _____

Whose PNR is displayed first? _____

Make the entry to send this PNR to the end of the queue to display the next PNR.

What entry did you make? _____

Whose PNR is next on the queue? _____

Make the entry to send this PNR to the end of the queue to display the next PNR.

Which segment has the status code "UN", meaning "unable to confirm"?

_____

Make the entry to sign off the queue and ignore the last PNR.

What entry did you use? _____

IV. What is the response when you try to sign on to Queue 2?

_____

V. What is the response when you sign on to Queue 40 and then Queue 70, immediately after?

_____

Why did you receive this response and how could it be avoided?

_____

Make the necessary entry to get off queue.

VI. Display the PNR for passenger Diane Wills, and enter a remark that will place the PNR on Queue 44 tomorrow with prefatory instruction code "18", "special meal".

What entry did you make?

_____

End the PNR.

Format Review

Queue Count	QC/	Count the number of PNRs on all queues
	QC/18	Count the number of PNRs on Queue 18
Queue Access	Q/20	Access Queue 20
Queue Exit	QXI	Simultaneously exit a queue and ignore PNR
	QXE	Simultaneously exit a queue and end PNR
Queue Placement	5Q-25APR65/11	Place a PNR on Queue 65 on April 25 with prefatory instruction code 11
	QP/74/60	Immediately place a PNR on Queue 74 with prefatory instruction code 60

LESSON **NINETEEN**

LEARNING OUTCOMES

At the end of this lesson, you should be able to:

• **Read status codes**
• **Change status codes**
• **Work through a PNR queue**
• **Delete a segment from a PNR**
• **Queue a PNR to a consolidator for ticketing**
• **Remove a PNR from queue**

In the online lesson, you have a chance to perform some queue tasks. One of the more common queue tasks is working through the schedule change queue. When an airline changes a flight's scheduled departure time, cancels a flight, or updates a passenger from waitlist status to confirmed status, the traveler must be informed, and "clean up" work may be required on the PNR.

When schedule changes occur, the airline will modify the status code in the flight segment and place the PNR on one of your agency's queues. This is usually the only way you will know about a flight change.

Recall that the standard status code for a confirmed flight booking is **"HK"**. When you see a status code other than "HK", it means a change has occurred on the flight, or the booking is not confirmed by the airline. You should always take the time to check the status code on all flights and SSR requests. Below are some common status codes:

KK	Carrier Confirming Request (flight is now confirmed, change to HK)
KL	Confirmed from Waitlist (same as KK)
TK	Schedule Change (the airline has changed the departure or arrival time; note new flight times and change status to HK)
SC	AA Schedule Change (same as TK)
UN	Unable - flight not operating (cancel flight, and book new one if airline has not provided an alternative)
WK	Was Confirmed (booking is no longer confirmed, cancel flight)

In the second exercise, you will work though a flight schedule change queue where you will see some of the codes listed above.

Review Questions

Changing Segment Status

1. On the Waitlist Queue, any segment having the status "KL" (confirmed from the waiting list) should be updated to the segment status of . . .

   _____

2. For a PNR on the Waitlist Queue, which segment should be canceled? Explain your answer.

   _____

3. To make a change segment status entry permanent, you must also . . .

    _____

4. Ending a transaction while on queue will always . . .

    _____

```
CONFIRM FROM WAITLIST
 1.4KOBIYASHI/AKIRO MR/KAWA MRS/KEISHI MSTR/HAYA MISS
 1 JL  74C 13DEC M NRTHNL HK4    930P   940A /DCJL*9V45TH /E
 2 JL  73C 25DEC J HNLNRT HK4    140P   440P 26DEC S /DCJL*9V45TH /E
 3 JL  71C 25DEC J HNLNRT KL4   1140A   240P 26DEC S /DCJL*9V45TH /E
TKT/TIME LIMIT
  1.TAW06DEC/
PHONES
  1.NRT03 4456 5314-A
  2.NRT03 4457 8891-H
GENERAL FACTS
  1.OSI JL MSTR KEISHI AGED 10 MISS HAYA AGED 7
RECEIVED FROM - MRS
A0A0.A0A0*AOL 1904/15NOV JMEERT
```

The following four questions are based on the above Sabre PNR, placed on the Waitlist Queue.

5. Why is this PNR on queue?

    _____

6. What entries update this PNR and remove it from the Waitlist Queue?

    _____

7. Assuming that this PNR is not the only PNR on the queue and is not the last PNR on queue, what would happen after you processed it?

    _____

8. If this is the last PNR on queue, what would happen after you processed it?

    _____

Supplementary Entries

Deleting a Segment

Sometimes an airline will cancel a flight. If you have a client booked on a flight that is no longer operating, the airline will queue the PNR to advise you of this situation. These flight segments must be removed from the PNR, but the standard segment cancellation entry should not be used. The standard cancellation entry sends a message back to the airline. When you delete a segment with the status "UN" (unable-does not operate) or "WK" (was confirmed), the following entry should be used.

.1XK

This entry removes a segment from a PNR without sending a message to the airline. The entry is used when the status of a flight is "UN" or "WK". The entry begins with a period for "change segment status", followed by the segment number and the two-letter status code "XK" for "delete".

Exercises

Don't forget to sign in to the emulator before beginning the exercises, and to sign out after finishing the last problem.

I. Make the entry to access Queue 18, the waitlist confirmation queue. Answer the following questions as you work through the queue. Use the first name in the name field for your received-from entry.

Whose PNR is the second on queue? _____

What entries did you make to process this PNR?

_____

Whose PNR is the next on queue? _____

What entries did you make to process this PNR?

_____

What was the response when you ended transaction on the last PNR on queue?

_____

II.   Make the entry to access Queue 5, a schedule change queue. Work through this queue. Segments with status "TK" (confirmed with time change) should be changed to "HK". Segments with status "UN" should be removed.

If a PNR has been placed on the queue more than once, remove the duplicate. Use the first name listed in the name field for each received-from entry. Answer the following questions as you work through the queue.

After working on the first two PNRs, whose PNR was displayed?

_____

Why was the PNR on queue again?   _____

What entry did you make to process this PNR?   _____

For the next PNR, for passenger Nadon, what segment needs to be changed to status HK and what was the status before you made this change?

_____

What is the status code of the other segment that needs action, and what needs to be done?

_____

What entry did you make to process this other segment?   _____

What was the response when you processed the last PNR on queue?

_____

Format Review

Changing Segment Status	`.1HK`	Change the status of segment 1 to "HK"
Segment Removal	`.1XK`	Delete segment 1 without sending message to airline
PNR Removal	`QR`	Remove a PNR from queue
Queue to a Branch Office	`QP/A0AZ99/11`	Queue a PNR to Queue 99 at branch office A0AZ

LEARNING OUTCOMES

At the end of this lesson, you should be able to:

•Use the Date Calculator
•Use the Number Calculator
•Use the Time Calculator
•Use the Temperature Calculator
•Use the KM/miles Calculator
•Use the Currency Calculator
•Display FLIFO
•Display Minimum Connecting Times
•Change Areas

This lesson covers some of the miscellaneous Sabre functions. These functions should be viewed as resources to help you with your main tasks.

Review Questions

Date Calculator

1. If your client, Mr. Orville Getz, is traveling to Warsaw on February 12, what entry would display the last possible return date for a 90-day maximum stay?

   _____

2. You have a client who will be joining a European tour starting on July 16. What entry displays the balance due date if payment is required by the tour operator 60 days prior to departure?

   _____

3. The entry T¤TUE will display dates for the next . . .

   _____

Time Calculator

4. What entry displays the local time in Rome, Italy (ROM)?

   _____

5. Suppose you are in Brussels, Belgium (BRU), and you want to find out by how many hours the time in Rio de Janeiro, Brazil (GIG) is behind your own time.

What would be the best entry to make to most easily determine the number of hours' time difference?

_____

6.   What entries calculate the following times?

If you started working on Lesson Thirteen at 2:45 p.m. and completed the lesson in 1 hour and 45 minutes, at what time did you finish?

_____

If Lesson Fourteen takes you 2 hours and 13 minutes to complete and you finish at 1:02 p.m., at what time did you start?

_____

Number Calculator

7.   Mr. Connors paid a deposit of $467.00 and has made two additional payments of $732.92 and $816.52. What entry calculates his total payments?

_____

8.   If the total cost for three passengers traveling to Germany is $4647.49, what entry displays the per-person cost?

_____

Temperature Calculator

9.   Your client is traveling to Honolulu, Hawaii this August, when the average temperature is 80 degrees Fahrenheit. What entry converts this to Celsius?

_____

10. Ms. Jones is traveling to Berlin on business next week. It is January, and the temperature is 28 degrees Celsius. What entry converts this to Fahrenheit?

_____

KM/Miles Calculator

11. The rental car your client is interested in offers 100 free miles. What entry converts this to kilometers?

_____

12. The distance between Montreal, Canada and Toronto, Canada is 545 kilometers. What entry converts this to miles?

_____

Currency Conversion

13. You have just returned from a holiday in Japan and would like to cash in your extra Japanese yen (JPY). If you have 2300 yen, what entry would determine the amount of local currency that the bank will give you in return?

_____

14. What entry would determine the equivalent amount in Great Britain pounds (GBP) for a fare of USD 500.00?

_____

FLIFO

15. Your client, Mrs. Habersham, is picking up her husband this evening at the airport. He is arriving from London on British Airways flight 113. What entry can you make to find out if the flight is arriving on time? Note: The date is required.

_____

Minimum Connecting Times

16. What entry determines the minimum connecting times for John F. Kennedy Airport in New York (JFK)?

_____

```
STANDARD.D/D...D/I...I/D...I/I.
ONLINE   1.00  1.15  1.45  2.00
OFFLINE  1.00  1.15  1.45  2.00
- IS ONE WAY  / IS BOTH WAYS
** OR * ARE ALL
AC-AC DD SUP    YUL - YOW
AC-AC DD SUP    YOW - YUL
AC-AC DD SUP    YUL - YYZ
AC-AC DD SUP    YYZ - YUL
AC-AC DD SUP    YUL - YVR
AC-AC DD SUP    YYZ - YOW¥
```

The following question is based on the above partial Sabre Minimum Connect Time Table.

17. The above display shows minimum connecting times for the John F. Kennedy airport in New York (JFK). What is the standard connecting time for an on-line flight from Ottawa, Canada to JFK, to Paris, France?

_____

Changing Work Areas

18. You are in the middle of building a new PNR when Mrs. Phillips calls to give you her new frequent-flyer number. How would you switch to work area "D" in order to retrieve her PNR without ignoring the unfinished PNR on which you are working?

_____

19. How would you then return to the area in which you were working on the new PNR? Assume that you began work in work area "A".

_____

Exercises

Don't forget to sign in to the emulator before beginning the exercises, and to sign out after finishing the last problem.

I. Make the entry to switch to work area "B".

    What is the response? _____

Return to work area "A". What entry did you make?

_____

II.   Suppose you have a group of 16 passengers each paying a fare of 1349.00. What is the total cost?

_____

III. Your client is scheduled to arrive in Paris at 5:00 p.m. What time will it be in Miami when she arrives?

_____

IV.   Your client owes $1492.00. She has made a deposit of $500.00 and two payments of $125.00 and $270.00. What does she owe?

_____

V.   Your client's fare has an advance purchase requirement of 30 days. The journey begins on May 22. What is the latest day your client can pay for his trip?

_____

VI.   A valued client has asked you to book a small inn in the Blue Mountains north of Sydney, Australia and has given you the telephone number. Is now an appropriate time to make the telephone call? Explain your answer.

_____

      What day is it in Sydney?

_____

VII. Your clients want to depart two weeks from Saturday. On what date will you display availability for their flights?

_____

VIII. What is the time difference between your home city and Hong Kong?

_____

IX. Convert the following:

30,000 Indian rupees into the currency of the United Kingdom _____

5,000 Kenyan shillings into the currency of Egypt _____

500.00 Australian dollars to the currency of Switzerland _____

X. Suppose that while on holiday in the resort town of Bali, Indonesia, you find one thousand Indonesian rupiah and decide to treat yourself. What is the equivalent amount in your own local currency?

Format Review

Date Calculation	T¤WED	Display the dates of the next four Wednesdays
	T¤14MAY¥60	Display the date 60 days after May 14
	T¤12JAN-21	Display the date 21 days before January 12
Time Calculation	T*VIE	Display the time and date in VIE
	T¤ETAKL/LAX	Display the time difference between AKL and LAX
	T¤ET1115FRA/MEL	Display the time in MEL when it is 11.15 in FRA
	T¤ET2245¥11535	Display the time 115 hours and 35 minutes after 22.45
	T¤ET2330-1215	Determine the time 12 hours and 15 minutes before 23.30
Temperature Conversion	T¤T20C	Convert 20 degrees Celsius to Fahrenheit
	T¤T88F	Convert 88 degrees Fahrenheit to Celsius

LESSON **TWENTY**

KM/Miles Conversion	T¤MIKM60	Convert 60 miles to kilometers
	T¤KMMI100	Convert 100 kilometers to miles
Currency Conversion	DC*CUR	Display a list of all currency codes and exchange rates
	DC*CUR/F	As previous, but only for countries that begin with the letter "F"
	DC¥CAD100/EUR	Convert 100 CAD into EUR
Number Calculation	T¤563.8¥28.72	Add 563.8 and 28.72
	T¤729-15.71	Subtract 15.71 from 729
	T¤199.50*3	Multiply 199.50 by 3
	T¤533/21	Divide 533 by 21
FLIFO	2AA123	Display flight information for AA flight 123 for today (today's date is required for some airlines, added to the end of the entry preceded with a slash)
Minimum Connecting Times	T*CT-JFK	Display minimum connecting times for JFK
Work Areas	¤C	Switch to work area "C"

LEARNING OUTCOMES

At the end of this lesson, you should be able to use:

•**DRS**
•**Format Finder**

This lesson covers the two major reference tools available for Sabre users: DRS and Format Finder. These resources are not housed within the Sabre GDS; they are separate programs that are accessed from a Sabre website and/or downloaded onto your desktop.

DRS

1. What do the letters "DRS" stand for?

   _____

2. Who provides the information found in DRS?

   _____

3. Is DRS part of the Sabre GDS? Explain your answer and explain how DRS is accessed.

   _____

   _____

   _____

4. The information in DRS is organized into six categories of vendor types: Airline, Bus, Car, Hotel, Insurance, Rail

   Identify the vendor type category you would select to answer the following questions. If the answer is not likely to be found in DRS, write "Not in DRS".

   Is satellite radio a special equipment option in Avis rental cars?

   _____

   How many berths are in Amtrak's Family Bedroom sleeper car?

   _____

   What is the PFC tax for each New York City airport?

   _____

   Does Singapore Airlines offer a Vegan meal?

   _____

What are the different room
types at Hilton Hotels?

_____

Is there a bus terminal located
near the Los Angeles airport?

_____

What is the cost of travel insurance
for a family traveling to China?

_____

What code is used to designate a cell (mobile)
phone number in the Sabre PNR?

_____

Format Finder

5. What type of information is found in Format Finder?

    _____

    _____

6. There are two versions of Format Finder. Describe each version and how it is
    accessed.

    _____

    _____

    _____

    _____

7. The Format Finder screen is divided into two panels.

    The left panel is used to ...

    _____

    The right panel is used to...

    _____

LESSON **TWENTY-ONE**

8. The Format Finder Home page appears when you first launch Format Finder or when you click on the "Home" button. The Home page is useful because the right panel contains . . .

    _____

    _____

9. Up to four tabs appear in the left panel: Contents, Index, Search, Favorites. Match each tab to the function described below.

    Tab Function   Tab Name

    Lists topics and keywords alphabetically
    without organizing them into categories   _____

    "Bookmarks" or saves Format Finder pages
    for easy retrieval   _____

    Allows you to enter a keyword, phrase or
    part of a Sabre format to look up information   _____

    Organizes Format Finder information into
    categories and lists each category
    alphabetically   _____

10. When you see a word or phrase underlined and in a different color in the right panel, this means . . .

    _____

    _____

11. Every content page in Format Finder shows a "topic locator number" in the upper-right corner, for example "carav003". What is the purpose of this alpha-numeric code and in which tab (Contents, Index, Search or Favorites) is it used?

    _____

    _____

    _____

LEARNING OUTCOMES

At the end of this lesson, you should be able to:

• **Explain what TIMATIC is used for**
• **Use Timaticweb**

In this lesson, you learn about an industry-wide reference source called Timatic. Timatic provides information about international air travel, and is based on the Travel Information Manual (TIM), published monthly by a consortium of airlines.

Airlines around the world use Timatic daily to determine if passengers have correct documentation for their journeys. It is also used by travel professionals to look up local health requirements, country facts, industry news and other relevant information pertaining to international air travel.

This lesson teaches you how to use Timaticweb, a GDS-independent web-based user interface to the vast Timatic database.

Timaticweb

1. Timaticweb contains five "areas" of travel information, each of which has a button in the red menu bar at the top of the Timaticweb page. These areas are:

    Passport, Visa and Health
    Country Information
    Travel Terms & Definitions
    City & Country Codes
    News

    What area of Timaticweb would you use to determine the following information?

    A client is traveling to the Bali and Lombok islands of the Indonesia archipelago. She wants to know what vaccinations are required and if malaria drugs are recommended.

    _____

    You've heard that some new passport regulations were introduced in the European Union (EU), and would like to find out more.

    _____

    What is a "BBC" or "laser visa?"

    _____

You're booking a client on a trip to Lagos, Nigeria and Johannesburg, South Africa, with a transit (connection) in London, England. You need to advise your client if a Visa is required for any of these three cities.

_____

Is a passport required for Canadian and US citizens vacationing in Nassau, Bahamas?

_____

You've been asked to become the office expert on travel to the Caribbean. You've traveled to the area a number of times, but need to gather some hard facts on the countries that comprise this area:

The currency used in each country _____

General geographical information for each country _____

The country code for each country _____

A list of city codes for all cities in that country _____